THE LOVE FITMAMA WAY:
Transforming the Core
of Motherhood

Jennifer Oliver

Dearest Kate,
Enjoy every second
of your loving journey ♡
Jennifer
Oliver

The Love FitMama Way:
Transforming the Core of Motherhood

Copyright © 2017 Jennifer Oliver

ISBN: 978-1-946978-34-9

All rights reserved.

All images are copyrighted by the author.

Disclaimer

This book is licensed for your personal enjoyment and education only. While best efforts have been used, the author and publisher are not offering legal, accounting, medical, or any other professional services advice and make no representations or warranties of any kind and assume no liabilities of any kind with respect to the accuracy or completeness of the contents and specifically disclaim any implied warranties of merchantability or fitness of use for a particular purpose, nor shall they be held liable or responsible to any person or entity with respect to any loss or incidental or consequential damages caused, or alleged to have been caused, directly or indirectly, by the information or programs contained herein.

Legal Notice

The reader is responsible for his or her own actions. Adherence to all applicable laws and regulations, including international, federal, state, and local governing professional licensing, business practices, advertising, and all other aspects of doing business in any jurisdiction is the sole responsibility of the purchaser or reader. Neither the author nor the publisher assumes any responsibility or liability whatsoever on the behalf of the purchaser or reader of these materials.

At times links might be used to illustrate a point, technique, or best practice. These will reference products I have found useful, but please do your own research, make appropriate comparisons, and form your own decisions as to which product will work best for you.

The information, ideas, and techniques in this book are not medical advice or treatment, but rather knowledge intended to assist the reader. It is the responsibility of the reader to seek treatment for any medical, mental, or emotional conditions that might warrant professional care.

Contents

Acknowledgments

This book is dedicated to you FitMama. I see you and the truth of who you are. Thank you for reading this book and opening your mind and your heart to what's possible for you when you start with love.

It is with a deepest bow of gratitude, I thank the people and the circumstances in my life that have brought me to this point of writing and publishing this book.

I am eternally grateful to my partner and soulmate in love and life, my husband, Chris. You raise me up and support me unconditionally with your heart and soul. Thanks for creating some sweet, tiny humans with me. Watching them blossom like flowers with you is my greatest gift in life.

To our precious girls, Kennedy and Presley, thank you for letting Mommy go away and work long hours to get this writing and editing completed. It felt like I was growing and birthing another baby, so thank you for honoring the space for me to do that, while loving me unconditionally and always showering me with love upon my return. Our times together are sacred to me, and I used my time away from you wisely, "with the FitMamas," as you say.

Thank you to my beautiful, selfless sister-in-law, Meredith Renwick, for doing the tough work of editing my thoughts and words into an actual book. I am eternally grateful for your selfless efforts and deep wisdom.

Thank you to my parents and siblings for raising me with love in every aspect to be who I am today.

Thank you to my brave and inspiring heart-centred mentors, Andy Ramsay and Marcus Bird. Thanks to your wisdom, I was able to extract mine.

Thank you to my beautiful and inspiring friends who date back more than 25 years and have influenced me in such positive ways as I grow, change, and, inevitably, move.

Thank you to friends and family around the globe, thank you for your loving support always. While we might not be physically together, you are never far in my heart.

Thank you, Tammy Blaze, for your many years of loving friendship and for taking the cover photo of my girls and I for this book.

To the many individuals who have always inspired me, lifted me up, shared with me, taught me, supported me, cared for me, believed in me, and demonstrated unconditional love and acceptance, I thank you. I am eternally grateful to have shared each moment we have had.

In no particular order, thank you OR, BR, TB, AB, TB, HW, AB, CR, JSC, RP, NC, RS, NC, KMG, SB, JO, GM, AG, EA, MW, SD, JM, DS, PA, WB, JP, JH, AB, JB, ZJ, DL, KY, CP, CR, KS, JB, AS, IM, BA, SO, GW, NZ, SN, AJ, QO, LF, BH, GO, BH, NW, LW, AR, MB, QH, MK, EG, TF, SG, GV, GB, WD, ET, JD, KV, SMH, JD, KB, BS, and HC.

Introduction

I am a firm believer in the idea that people can create the things they wish existed in this world. I believe that we are not victims of circumstance but brilliant, beautiful beings who have and create experiences we can live, learn, and grow through. I believe we can choose our thoughts, actions, and reactions to manipulate certain outcomes in our lives. Do things always go as we'd want? Nope, but that's life. We don't control all the elements. And your mama probably told you this already . . . "life isn't fair."

You can create something from nothing but an idea. All things sprout first from an idea or a tiny seed that's been planted within us along our journey, and we can see by looking back at our own lives that *thoughts* can become *things*. Technology has been driving the speed at which humans create, and it looks like things are going to only speed up.

Hold your hat, are you ready for this ride?

The Love FitMama Way was born out of a need. At first it was to connect others close to me with the information I was learning, so they too could treat their bodies, postpartum, with self-care and self-love. Then, I kept seeing the need on a larger scale. While working as a fitness instructor and personal trainer, I realized how little understanding was out there about how the core works, and how many people were inadvertently harming themselves deeply (myself included), with potentially long-term consequences—all in the name of "getting" or "staying fit." I realized that what I knew from studying fitness, psychology, and human habit formation was not widely known and thus wasn't getting out to those who would benefit from it most, postpartum moms.

I started digging deeper into what the literature in anatomy, physiology, psychology, social, and practical science was stating and started seeing that this information needed a bigger platform. Had I known what I discovered in my research even three months before, I might not have given myself an injury that burdened me for almost three years with chronic back pain.

After I injured myself, due to a weak and dysfunctional core I wasn't taking proper care of, it became urgent for me to learn more. The less I could do physically due to pain, the more this pain acted like a catalyst for me to search deeper. Its dull ache and daily stabbing with any movement begged me stay on the path when I wanted to shy away from focusing on the deep muscles and follow the status quo in the fitness world. I felt a deep drive to uncover more detail on how interconnected the core was with being a new mom. The Love FitMama movement took over and even if I tried, the wave was too big to stop me on my quest.

With this book, I am here to help educate more FitMamas on the what, how, and why of the deep inner core, both physically and metaphysically (what you can and cannot see). These topics are becoming more mainstream, thankfully, but most of the concepts I teach usually receive a big sigh of relief or deep breath with a comment like, "Why did nobody tell me this before?"

Before I really dug into the core, I was just focusing on more of the same that is found in the fitness industry: different/harder workouts and calorie/macro/restriction, and obsessing about these tiny details with my clients. Restriction, deprivation, and pain will never be long-term, sustainable, sanity-saving solutions.

The science I present in the book shows this; it isn't just my opinion.

Within the pages of this book, you will find research and tools that will support you, educate you, enlighten you, and clarify what the best course of action is for you. You will learn what your body really needs from you; what your mind, heart, and gut need from you too. Your needs change daily, and the Love FitMama Way™ (LFM Way) will teach you how to get into the flow of life and truly transform the core of what it means to be a FitMama going through this journey of motherhood.

When it comes to being a mom, I am sure you can agree with me that *more* time and focused attention to your fitness and nutrition were NOT side effects of having a baby. More like, all your needs dropped off the list and you forgot to look in the mirror or shower for a few weeks/months/years at a time. The LFM Way™ will show you that whatever you truly desire, though, is attainable in both the short and long term.

Do you really believe that anything is possible for you? That belief is the ultimate first step. As I connected the core rehabilitation research to the data around the mind-body connection and neuroplasticity, I was deeply fascinated with what was possible. Not only could new moms rehab their cores postpartum through proper exercise and breathing, but they could actually be stronger than they ever were before having babies! The possibilities thereafter are endless due to the neurological changes that take place. We can take control, and we don't have to be victims of motherhood by way of leaking urine, back pain, prolapse, or other core dysfunctions.

Through this, I learned not only how to strengthen and relax my own deep core and heal my back injury but also how to support you, FitMama. The lack of core understanding is evident, the more I see other moms struggling with weight loss after childbirth, struggling with looking in the mirror, and struggling with slowing down and resting, while seeing a belly and a body that doesn't resemble the one they knew. The struggle is real with establishing self-care, nutrition, and fitness routines with ever-changing schedules, balancing being a new mom, and taking care of so many responsibilities, but I knew there was a better way. It's the LFM Way™.

At FitMama, I always say, "Abs are made on the cushion," which signifies the importance of spending time quietly breathing on a meditation cushion or pillow (or anywhere) to support yourself. Creating and living in a body you love after having kids is usually more about what you DON'T do, than what you DO. This book reveals it all.

I go through the do's and the don'ts throughout this book, and I share many FITMAMA FOUNDATIONS™ with you. I think you might find them to be counter to what you have heard all your life. FitMama likes to stand conventional thinking on its head and take a look at things with a new perspective.

I wrote this book to support FitMamas to rehabilitate their cores (your belief systems, values, and thoughts are part of the *core* of you too). If you are looking for a way to re-establish your sense of calm and confidence, around your core lifestyle habits, thoughts, behaviors, and beliefs, in a way that feels good, day in and day out, then this book is for you. The scientific data I share with you in simplistic ways will help you understand the evidence for the body and the brain's potential for change and transformation in ways you never thought possible.

Be prepared to open up and blow your mind with possibilities, regardless of where you feel you are today. I coupled this data with the positive psychology research about flow, mindset, emotions, mindfulness, habits, self-awareness, and self-regulation (aka willpower), and the Love FitMama Way™ was born. While it might sound like a lot, I assure you this book is to be used as a guide. The research won't lie, and the journey is laid out for you throughout the book. Follow the LFM Way™ and you will be rewarded by your own pure unconditional love, gratitude, and light shining bright for all the world to bask in.

I saw and continue to see incredible research being done furthering our understanding of the mind-body connection that forms the basis of the education and support provided to millions of FitMamas around the globe. I am so glad you are one of them.

As I implemented these diverse, but interrelated, areas together for my private FitMama clients, incredible things were happening for them.

Everything I studied just kept me digging deeper into more topics regarding being a FitMama. I realized that it's what preceded the behaviors of eating healthy, exercising, or any form of self-care that was the most important transformation, not the behavior itself. It is your mindset, heart set, and lens with which you see the world that play a more crucial role in the vitality of your core—the core of your being. It's your own mind-body-soul connection to *yourself* that is a defining factor. For yourself, can you honestly answer, "Do I have and demonstrate true, unconditional love for myself?"

In this book, I call on you to dig deeper into yourself. There can be comfort, flow, and great ease about your self-care routines, it doesn't have to be a struggle. The LFM Way™ will take you far below the superficial surface of the usual before and after pictures on Instagram, #fitspo, #cleaneating, or #abs ideals. How many of those people are working at sculpting their bodies in an aggressive, demanding, negatively charged, and militant way?

How many contestants from *The Biggest Loser* TV show have kept the weight off years later? Spoiler alert: almost NONE. They might have LOST weight (when working out for hours a day and being fed very little food), but losing weight isn't most people's issue. It's keeping the weight off. It's living a healthy lifestyle *long term*. It's NEVER a magic pill. It's easy to desire the (workout and meal plan) perfection we think we see online, but it is a futile quest. Seeking perfection is a sure way to drive yourself completely nuts.

Without the deeper foundations of the Love FitMama Way™, knowing *what* to do (eat this, run that far) is different from truly embodying HOW to do those things in a sustainable way in YOUR life right now. Actually taking action and DOING them is that massively scary (and lifelong) practice that so many never get to after having babies, most often because the perfect circumstances never present themselves.

If you remember nothing else, one of the most important takeaways from the pages of this book is that the perfect circumstances WILL NEVER present themselves. But it's action that needs to take place anyway, regardless of how much you "feel like it." Action on repeat is that necessary step that makes it all come together for true and lasting transformation.

You might have seen this already in your own FitMama journey, but because our brains act (in some ways) like computers, running automatic updates and simple programs, it's all too common to fall back into old habits. The habits that "feel" easy. This happens due to old neural pathways you've followed throughout the years that contribute to the automated programs that dictate your life.

Our brains want to keep things simple, so they create these "programs." This makes it easier on us. The programs say, "Wake up, shower, eat breakfast, have coffee, drive to work," and keep things running smoothly and allow us to think about other things while the program runs itself.

Through this book, I challenge you NOT to live your life by the programs you have set up by default. Start to recognize the programs you realize no longer serve you. So, you can choose to create new programs that do. I outline the tools needed to do just this, and they are ALL things I do and have done.

You might not be ready for (or want) any changes in your life or your body, and I am not here to tell you that you need to change, but it all starts with understanding the *why* behind taking care of your core and yourself (and who you're doing it for in the short and long term . . . Hint: it's YOU). By taking small, bite-sized steps each day, they add up to big leaps forward to living and being the you that you most desire to be. FitMama follows the "kaizen with Jen" principle of continuous improvement, centered on realistic, positive, incremental changes.

This natural connection between Mother Nature and the mind-body approach that FitMama takes is where the tagline #StrengthenYourRoots was born. We get into the familial, cultural, and societal norms that might have shaped the way you see your body and yourself and how to shift these perspectives to enable you to thrive. We dive below the surface of the fitness and diet industry to discover what's truly holding you back from following through on your goals or desires. We talk about the myths and the research-backed "how-tos" behind embracing, nurturing, and enjoying your body, loving it from now onwards, rehabbing it postpartum (no matter how many years later), and reconnecting to you. You will gain a deeper understanding of how this tremendous transition into motherhood offers a unique and priceless platform for a beautiful, meaningful, and deep transformation from within.

Don't underestimate the transformative power of becoming a mother! You're like a caterpillar turned into a stunningly beautiful butterfly. You might just be looking elsewhere and aren't seeing it yet.

You have the potential to rewire your brain and your body, just by reading this book, staying open-minded, asking yourself the questions posed within, and following it up by putting it into practice in your own life. This is where the real magic will happen for you.

1. Stay open-minded.

2. Ask questions.

3. Take action.

This is the one, two, three punch of getting the most out of this book.

Go forth and be aware of how these pages before you can open up a wildly beautiful world you didn't know was possible. If you've ever felt dissatisfied, displeased, or destroyed by your motherhood journey or wondered how to love your body or love your life, this is the book for you. It's not about loving yourself and your life on some future date, when you achieve "X" weight or goals—because that day never comes when you're always searching for it. It's about loving it all NOW.

One day at a time.

Yes, you can. I will show you how.

This is your journey and it starts now.

I share personal stories of my two births, my recoveries, what I learned, my journey rehabbing my own core, what I knew and didn't know, how I injured my back and ended up in the hospital twice in one week, and what followed when I had to quit my job but still take care of my two girls, ages one and three at the time. I share how you can choose a better road to go down than I did, if you aren't feeling your best right now.

The Love FitMama Way™ is a journey, and through the principles outlined in this book, you will see a formula come together that will allow you to build a strong foundation deep in your core for the remainder of your life. Once you are a FitMama, you are always a FitMama. It is a mindset and a lifestyle that honors you, and you can make the choice to live from there daily.

It *is* a daily choice.

By implementing the tools in this book, you will discover how good it feels to acknowledge that all you need is within you. That you can safely and unapologetically love yourself and be yourself. That you deserve love and plenty of it, from yourself most especially. You will discover that time is, in fact, on your side, if you let yourself truly and deeply *feel* the experiences you're living. Without escaping or avoiding, facing the physical or nonphysical fears you have will liberate you long term. And last, by the end of this book, you will know that you are worth it.

This is a message of love, hope, faith, grace, trust, and living by your values and virtues as a mom, leader, soul, and human on this planet. You honoring you allows others to do the same. Through your own self-love and self-care practices, you can be a beacon of light for your children, family, friends, and all those around you so that we can collectively raise a generation of boys and girls to become men and women who love and respect their bodies and their lives.

Being a FitMama all starts with LOVE.

Unconditional self-love is a birthright and a gift that is available to you for the taking. Within these pages, I will unveil the way—the Love FitMama Way™. Thank you for being here.

Please find more resources online at
http://www.jenoliver.com, http://www.lovefitmama.com and
join the supportive FitMama Facebook group at
http://facebook.com/groups/lovefitmama or
FitMama Global at
https://www.facebook.com/JenOliverFitMama/.

Part 1

Embrace: Heed Your Needs

CHAPTER 1

Go within to Flourish FitMama

"The secret of change is to focus all your energy not fighting the old, but on building the new."

—Socrates

There are few things as life altering as becoming pregnant and having a baby. I don't know if there is bigger news that you could share with yourself, your partner, or your family. It's a massive change. And we humans aren't known to be particularly good with change.

We tend to resist and fear change, even when we've invited the change ourselves. We want it on our terms, so we hold ourselves back from fully embracing the change.

FITMAMA FOUNDATION: Acceptance is lighter than resistance.

With my first pregnancy, as I prepped in my mind for our new bundle to be ready for her birth day, I used to say to my husband, "Do you know that we are about to get a new and fun little roommate that we made and who is not going to leave for like the next 20 years?!" This would totally change the dynamic of our family, of everything we'd known so far.

We used to laugh about it then, but looking back, that was just one of so many incredible realizations we had en route to becoming parents. Regardless of what we were really feeling—nervous, excited, frightened—the truth was that we just had to accept that massive changes were going to happen, and we could choose to embrace them or resist them. We always have that choice.

It's all too easy to hope that this blip on the radar won't change much about your current life. For example, I have heard so many moms say things like, "You're not going to see me clutter my house up with baby things; my house is going to stay clean and organized. I don't have to fall in line with these mom stereotypes."

While I am all about not wanting to fall into stereotypes, this type of comment is really about resisting change and deciding that you are going to control all the changes that are coming. I am sure my hubby and I said something like this to each other a few times, but if you view even one video from the FitMama FitBlitz program, you can see my living room where I shot the videos—there in plain sight are my kids' trampoline, books, toys, and everything else. I let go of that expectation and life went on.

If you too said this before you had your kids, have you changed your mind since then? Are there other judgments that have since changed? We can choose to evolve with each new experience. If you haven't changed your mind and still find yourself judging others often, consider seeing it as an example of resistance and look curiously at your life to see if you have the "things need to be . . . perfect/on my schedule/just the way I want them" mentality. It shows up in many ways.

Opening yourself up to whatever is to come, instead of reflexively projecting fears and mentally rehearsing worst-case scenarios, is an ideal way to approach impending change, especially when we have little control over it.

Taking this approach can feel counterintuitive, as it is often the opposite of what we are used to, if we are constantly trying to control the environment around us.

This concept is a similar one that my husband (a coach, professor, and speaker) says often to his coaches, students, and players (and now our girls), "Be open-minded, suspend judgment, and stay curious." This piece of wisdom actually applies to all areas of life.

Childbirth: From Dreams to Reality

When I was first pregnant, I loved reading pregnancy books and daydreaming about what my baby would be like. I wondered if she would be "spirited" or "textbook," as Tracy Hogg, known as "the baby whisperer," describes.

I spent almost every night reading about how my baby was developing, and it became clear that everything she was doing to grow ears, arms, toes, and teeth was being done WITHOUT my controlling any of it.

However, I also recall, vividly, how terrified I was of actually giving birth. It was all balloons and birthday parties in my mind, until I got to the scary idea of pushing a human out of my vagina. THAT was way more than I could wrap my head around, while my little one was growing from the size of a raspberry to an avocado to a banana and then a watermelon. ("Did that app just say I have something the size of a WATERMELON in my belly?") Yikes.

I recall meeting my doula, Rhea, in a Walkerville, Ontario, café when I was about six months pregnant with my first. My belly was really starting to grow. The impending doom of giving birth was on the horizon and Rhea was recommended to me by my naturopathic doctor (ND). As fate would have it, her advice had the potential to change my whole birth experience.

She wasn't surprised when I told her I didn't want to read the parts of the pregnancy book that explained birth prep or actually birthing. She wasn't saying, "You should do this or you should do that," when I told her I was unlikely to ever watch a video of another woman birthing, just to prep for my own. It horrified me, and I felt it was completely irrelevant. I knew I didn't need to see another woman responding in her own way when I was going to be doing something that my body had the innate wisdom to figure out on its own, and I could form my own reaction to.

I just explained how scared I was of the whole thing. Looking back, my fear stemmed only from ignorance and being naïve to possibility. I didn't have experience being around birth. I had only heard horror stories. I didn't know any terms, other than C-section and epidural, and I knew I wanted neither. Ignorance, it turns out, is not bliss.

But detailed birth plans, Rhea said, are not necessary. I see this too with regard to nutrition and fitness. We get set on specific plans, and nothing ever goes according to plan. Then our first reactions are regret, blame, shame, or self-rejection of some sort. This can come up for many people as even more stressful. And it almost always leads to a worse outcome and consistent self-sabotage, which becomes a habit and a way of life.

That being said about plans, *planning* itself is essential.

In direct response to my fear of birthing, my doula simply and calmly communicated exactly what I needed to hear. Let me explain the terms, walk you through the process, and be there to hold your hand IF you want it. She said to have no expectations that birth would be this way or that, and *stay curious* about what my own personal birth story would be.

Stay curious.

As you probably experienced, everyone loves to share their birth story with you—and, not surprisingly, I heard a lot of "horror" stories. "It was the worst pain ever." "Take the drugs! Why wouldn't you?" "My labor was 77 hours long!" What is a poor, naïve, unaware, pregnant woman to do?

Not surprisingly, this is a tough point and many women give up their power by not becoming educated and curious about what other possibilities there are for them—such as a quick, drug-free, calm, birthing experience. Which was exactly what I ended up having.

Both my births were unlike any of the stories I had heard. Those fear stories didn't prepare me whatsoever. I will share my experiences within the pages of this book, but, in short, on the day I was due, my water broke about 5:00 a.m. in my sleep. I woke and decided to start vacuuming to move things along, as I was told by a close friend that if you sit after your water breaks, you are more likely to stall in labor (not desirable)!

After 20 minutes of vacuuming (you might come to learn that happens as rarely as I give birth), I started noticing cramps and then things came on strong and fast. My midwives told me it was time to go to the hospital, as I was already having the urge to push. No one expected this quick for a first labor, and we were sent into a tailspin, rushing to the hospital, hoping I didn't give birth en route.

Hubby drove to the hospital with me lying across the back seat gripping the door handle and writhing in pain, trying to breathe in and out of each contraction. When I got there (about 9:30 a.m.), the midwife checked me, told me my cervix was dilated 10 cm, and got me into a room. Well, luckily without complications, after about 45 minutes of pushing, I gave birth to my first daughter at 10:26 a.m. All was excellent with her, and we were able to be discharged and were home by 3:00 p.m. that same day.

Sadly, as fabulous and incredible as this experience was for me, I have rarely shared the details, because these are not the stories being shared readily. Stories like this receive "I hate you" looks and comments like "That's not normal; that wouldn't ever happen to me." Misery loves company and nobody wanted mine.

Now, when people ask me about how I found giving birth, I say truthfully, "It was one of the most incredible experiences of my life. You will love it. It is blissful." And yes, I get weird looks, and then people just think, "Oh, she's just saying that; she's always positive," or "Well, you must be a weird freak of nature." I don't discount this thought, but I don't think it was the reason for my fabulous birth experiences either.

Little did I know, though I thought I got off easy in my births, the greatest pain I've ever felt and the toughest climbs I had to endure were yet to come.

Heed Your Needs

It's so easy to think that we can "do it all" as moms, and we want pregnancy and birthing to be one more task we can check off the list, and then we get back to doing everything that we were doing before. Controlling these times, though, and attempting to control our own body's functions, our baby's needs, and how our body looks can be completely draining. These actions are guaranteed to cause more stress and anxiety, both short and long term.

When we feel like we need rest or sleep but don't take it because we have other things to do—laundry, taking care of other kids, cooking, working, etc.—we start to undermine our own needs and feel that putting others' needs before ours is more important. We all know that to be at our best for others, we need to take care of ourselves first. But, as with most things, it's easier said than done.

This self-care concept of "heed your needs" is the starting point for my private FitMama clients. Often, as women, we are raised and socialized to care more about what others think of us than what we think of ourselves. We want to be thought of as kind, generous, thoughtful, caring, and always there for others. Many years ago, I would say, "yes, of course!" with enthusiasm to doing things I didn't really want to do because I felt "bad" saying no, and I really had no good reason why. So, I would overschedule, spend time with people who didn't light me up, and do things for others at my expense.

Heeding your needs is about taking the time and space to care for yourself, when you need it, and not waiting until it fits someone else's schedule. Yes, with young babies, we are at their beck and call, but often we have help or loved ones who want to help us, but we don't take it because we "feel bad asking" or just plow through the pain, exhaustion, and moodiness because "it has to be done."

Taking the time and the space that you need during pregnancy and postpartum (once you're postpartum, following childbirth, you're always postpartum), even if it takes years to get back to doing some of the things that you were doing before, if ever, is worth it. It's not about how you look; it's about how you feel. And when you can start shifting this mindset and tune in to your feelings and then honor them, it is showing your body the love and respect it needs.

Your body is like your car. But you only get one in this lifetime. You can choose to put in low-grade fuel, not clean it or take care of it, and, eventually, it won't look, feel, or function the same as it was originally intended. Your personality, life, and soul need a vehicle to live on this planet, and that is your body.

You were blessed with your body, and if it doesn't look or feel the way you want it to, you can start to take action by shifting the way you think about it. Creating a better, more intimate relationship with yourself and your body, built on a foundation of gratitude, reverence, self-respect, and love is a recipe for everything you've ever dreamed of.

This is all about patience, presence, and permission.

Allow yourself to gain a new perspective on the entire life change that just went on. Keep that place with a calm, cool, connectedness that comes only from being alone. And see, with compassion and love, that this incredibly beautiful transition of becoming a mother more resembles a caterpillar turning into a beautiful butterfly, than a natural disaster that can never be undone.

FITMAMA FOUNDATION: Tune inward for insights and solutions.

It's so common for us to look outside ourselves for the answers. What should I eat? What should I do for exercise? How can I get my body and my life back? These are some of the most common questions I get, and while I can educate you on the safest way to do things to maximize your recovery, everyone is different. Just as life coach Tony Robbins would say, you are your own guru. You have all the answers for what your body needs at any given time; all you need to do is tune inward and quiet down all the "life noise" to hear the messages.

Ask yourself, "Where do these themes show up in my life?"

If you are truly here and ready to heed your needs, ask yourself this question next, "What do I need right now?" (Keep reading, if the first thing you need is a nap). Do this after your pregnancy journey and birth story. "I need this now." "What I need now is . . . " Complete that statement.

Because if you don't know what you need, nobody else will be able to help you.

We're so conditioned to escape our current moods, feelings, and desires by distraction. When we have an idle moment, or feel physical/emotional discomfort, without even thinking, most of us will reflexively look for an escape. We start scrolling through social media, eating, drinking, or distracting ourselves with other people, when our own needs are what really need our focus.

I have seen it time and time again where moms will say, "No! I got this, I don't need help. No, you just rest," to their partner or other willing helping hands. I did it myself. We think that by telling others to rest and relax, typically our partners, we will be able to feel more rested. This simply isn't the case. What brews up instead is resentment. We can only sit ourselves on the backburner for so long until our own needs boil over and demand attention.

FITMAMA FOUNDATION: Ask yourself often what you need, so you are able to vocalize it to others.

Whether your pregnancy and birth stories involve loss, infertility, complications, surgeries, adoption, surrogacy, or other experiences, while you peel back the layers of this onion that is you and what you have gone through to be a mom, your children are a gift to you and they are not your property. They were given to you, to offer you an opportunity to be a leader. To lead from your open heart within, to lead yourself first, and then to this next generation of incredible humans.

The next few chapters are going to delve deeper into how you can get into this place of consistent, present-moment awareness, how to more deeply cultivate patience within yourself, and how to give yourself the permission you need to trust in yourself and allow yourself to truly LIVE in each day. Not by others' expectations or how you expected it to be when you imagined it in the past, but instead allowing life to just unfold and flow.

LOVE FITMAMA CHAPTER TAKEAWAY

1. Write your pregnancy journey and birth story in detail, journal it all out. "Reflection is the mother of wisdom" (Robin Sharma).

2. Ask yourself constantly throughout the day, "What do I need?" Don't wait for someone else to ask.

3. Be open-minded, suspend judgment, and stay curious

CHAPTER 2

Patience: One Step at a Time

"Have patience with all things, But, first of all with yourself."

—Saint Francis de Sales

I so often hear moms say, "I can't wait to get my body back," or "I can't wait until I am done breastfeeding so I can lose weight," or "I can't wait until my kids are sleeping through the night." It's the idea of not being able to wait, of getting back to the way things were before, things were before, or rushing to some hypothetical, ideal future.

I discussed in the first chapter about heeding your needs and embracing what is. The fact is that your old normal is not your new normal. Life with babies and children changes things. And this is a good thing!

FITMAMA FOUNDATION: Your body never went anywhere.

The idea of wanting to get your body back is common, but your body hasn't gone anywhere. Your body is doing what it's meant to be doing at this time in your life. And we start to force things, like schedules, or cutting off breastfeeding because we want to diet or run, or thinking our boobs are too big or flopping around too much—they are our babies' food source! Breastfeeding is one of the most nourishing and nurturing things that we can ever give to a small child. And if we can hold off on our impatience to get back to running, dieting, drinking, or doing whatever it is that we think we should be doing, we can start to reframe things in our minds. Realize that this time is fleeting.

There will come a time when your child is sleeping through the night and she will want nothing to do with you and snuggling in your bed. That time will come sooner than you think. As you might expect, you will not have a 15 year old with a soother in his mouth, or a 20 year old that isn't potty trained, or a 12 year old who wants to breastfed. And when you start to get back to that mindset of appreciation and reverence for your body and the miracle of you being a mother, you can start to enjoy the moments as they come, without wishing them away. Whether you waited one year or five years postpartum to run, or to get your "body back," so to speak, or to feel back to "normal," it's truly a short time in the large scheme of things.

Ask yourself, "Why am I placing so much importance on how my body looks anyway?" This was an issue I had to explore in myself too. I thought that because I was a trainer, a health and fitness professional, and a mind-body coach, I had to look a certain way. I thought if I didn't, I wouldn't look like I "walked the talk." The gyms, studios, and fitness centers have made being fit more than about health, it's become more about vanity.

I definitely pushed myself too hard so I could maintain the fitness look. I never judged others based on how they looked, but I was harshly judging myself during this time. I was fixated on getting my body looking like it was in tip-top shape. Because I loved exercise, I enjoyed the gym, and I loved the routines it allowed me to create in my life, I figured there was no harm done.

The problems for me—and for many FitMamas I have met, talked to, and worked with—were not having the patience to know my body needed time to physically recover. That it just wasn't the same body that I had before I became pregnant. It was a supercharged, amazing body after what it had been through—but it needed time to rehabilitate. I needed to take the time to rebuild the foundation of my deep core that got its world rocked while I was growing a human (two, in my case) and pushing it out of my body.

At the time, I thought I understood the core. I had been training myself and others for almost 15 years at that point. I loved to read, learn, and take more workshops and certifications. How could it be so different training after having a baby than before? There wasn't much out there mainstream that really got into what was going on in the deep core. Wait six weeks; do some heel slides and breathing; start building back up to planks, crunches, and Russian twists; right? WRONG! I began getting debilitating back pain. My lower back hurt all day, no matter what I did. I thought I needed to strengthen more. So, I lifted heavier and kept on pushing. Finally, nothing was helping, so I started really investigating. And the deeper I researched, the more I found. It was imperative that I start sharing what I learned with others.

I began practicing breathing techniques, and I learned about core breathing from the three brilliant women who founded Bellies Inc. I learned more about how the anatomy and physiology of the core changes with pregnancy and birth. The more I found, the more I found what I was doing wrong. What I was doing that wasn't supporting my core, most especially my lower back pain.

The more research I did, the louder the message got. Rest and proper retraining of the core were needed.

The research available nowadays is incredible. I started understanding more about how the core worked and how core breathing was the single most important exercise a woman can do through pregnancy and postpartum to pre-hab and rehab the core.

Breathing? That was it? The answer was simple and so I got started.

Just Breathe

When we breathe deeply, it calms our nervous systems. And as new moms (or simply as humans), we are almost always in a high-alert state.

When we start to quiet the mind and breathe deeply into our core, it allows us to stop and see more clearly.

For me, I started to get out of that old mentality that I "should" look a certain way, or feel a certain way, or that I should be doing a certain thing by a certain time. Patience with your body is about getting out of that mentality completely and realizing that these pressures we put on ourselves are not grounded in any reality or reason. These pressures are what we "think" we should be doing. We can choose to think another way.

When we can start to calm our brains and our nervous systems, we are in a calmer frequency of brain wave activity and are closer to that calm we feel while we are drifting off to sleep. Breathing alone can be effective, not only for core recovery but also recovering from the exhaustion we commonly feel as new moms.

It took me longer than I care to admit to really sink into the idea that I had to relax. I hurt myself by using a sacroiliac (SI) joint belt too hard around my hips. I wasn't given instructions when it was prescribed, and I used all my might to tighten it around my hips to support me. One day—I only wore it one day and then I woke up the next morning and knew something wasn't right. Two days later, I got out of bed and fainted from pain only to be rushed to the hospital for tests. I couldn't walk. I had literally pinched and twisted my own hips out of alignment. And then, because it hurt so much, I couldn't bear to feel that again, my body reacted in complete shock by tensing up the muscles of my upper glutes and lower back in a syndrome called tension myositis syndrome, TMS for short, coined by Dr. John E. Sarno, a medical doctor and pioneer in the field of physical medicine and rehabilitation.

My husband heard radio personality Howard Stern talking about it. I knew Stern was into meditation, so it seemed like a worthwhile lead, as I was open to learning anything. It piqued my curiosity, so I read Sarno's book, *Healing Back Pain: The Mind-Body Connection.* It was interesting, because it was almost the exact same thing that my myomassologist (also known as the pain whisperer) Janna Clapp-Arsenault had been working on with me for the prior six months.

We had been addressing my fear about the pain and holding my body hostage by the pain experience that my muscles had memorized. I literally caused my own injury, which turns out to be something that could have healed fairly quickly. But because of the emotion of fear and the busy mom and entrepreneur mentality that I was carrying, the load was so strong, and my back wouldn't relax. No therapy worked. I was so mad! And this made the pain worse. Until the force was too great, I had to surrender.

Nothing could be done except diving deeper into the fear and slowing down enough to let me move and cry through it. It brought me to my knees in both physical and emotional pain. There was the self-blame, the regret, and the shame about doing this to my body. What I had put my family and myself through because of my back pain.

Now, in the aftermath, after reflection, the experience has truly been worth it. I have realized the value of rest, relaxation, and finding harmony in both the push and the pull. It's allowed me to slow down enough to stop and smell the roses multiple times a day.

Current research exploring brain wave activity, measured by electroencephalography (EEG), shows that the high frequency, beta wave state is where we spend most of our time. We spend time thinking, over-thinking, planning, and worrying about our body and mind's needs: I'm thirsty, hungry, tired, bored, annoyed, frustrated, etc. We spend our days thinking about who did what to us and who or what we didn't like about our life or the people in it. We focus on who hurt us and why, or who we hurt and how we feel bad or guilty for saying this or not doing that. We focus on controlling our lives and the people in them. This is most of our waking hours!

The lower frequency, beta state and moving into the alpha wave state is where we start to feel calmer, more relaxed, and more connected to our present state and less reactive to each little need of the body and the mind. As we continue to lower our brain wave activity as we fall asleep, we go through theta waves, and then the slowest, deepest state of sleep we reach is the delta wave state.

This can be actively achieved through meditation. This simple exercise, sitting quietly and breathing, is what I'm urging you to do day in and day out. My fitness prescription (though I can give you a more advanced version eventually) all begins with breathing. Some people don't move beyond that for years. Yes, years! Me included.

The beautiful thing is that we don't have to try to get good at it overnight. It truly is a practice that we get to do day in and day out throughout our lives. Our breath is a direct path to calm and strength. We don't have to feel like it's going to be another thing to add to our busy day. It can just incorporate into our day: 10 minutes of silence, focusing on our breathing once or twice a day. We all deserve this.

FITMAMA FOUNDATION: Create a daily practice of quiet, mindful breathing.

To cultivate more patience, it is important to begin this whole process by consciously controlling our brain wave activity. This is something we can control! Breathing and mindfulness are the way.

First, by calming the nervous system, we help our bodies realize that we are not on a race against the clock. That no matter how much we want things to be different, we can be with them now, just as they are. Whether we "lose the baby weight" we think we need to lose in nine months, nine years, or never, it needn't put us in a state of panic.

In the grand scheme of things, you are here on the planet for approximately no time at all, so make the time count, and don't waste needless energy on worrying so much about the belly roll or thighs that are bigger than someone else's. Someone else's will always be smaller, and someone else's will always be bigger.

Focusing on more meaningful things in life will calm the nervous system too. As new moms, new dads, and new families, we want to start connecting deeper into ourselves by slowing down a few notches and realizing our babies only just need our love, our nurturing, and our presence in this moment. And we too need that from ourselves.

So, starting now, notice your breathing, and start taking time daily to check inside with you. Start your day with some deep core breathing. Practice the Pearl Pull-Ups™, taught at FitMama, to reconnect your core, strengthen, and address the common "leaking bladder" issue so many moms experience. Here are my instructions for how to do them.

Pearl Pull-Ups™

- While seated comfortably on a dining chair, center your pelvic floor below your torso with your pelvis in a neutral position.

- With your feet planted firmly on the ground, begin with deep breaths, inhaling into your lower ribcage and lungs, expanding them left to right. As you inhale, think about relaxing your pelvic floor and releasing any tension.

- Just as you are about to exhale at the top of the breath, imagine a tiny pearl at the opening of your urethra (where you urinate) that you pick up and pull up toward your navel. It should feel like a lift in front and then a zipping up of the midline. While you are pulling the pearl upward, exhale forcefully while pursing your lips.

- As the pearl zips up to your navel, imagine your front hip bones coming closer together. You can place your fingers to feel the activation in your transversus abdominis muscles just inside from your hip bones toward the midline.

- Each time you inhale, release the pearl and relax, and then on the next exhale, pick it back up and zip back up the midline.

- Even if you don't completely feel the muscles moving at first, it takes some time for the body to catch up, keep allowing the brain to send these signals to the body. Soon you will feel a deep core reconnection, strengthening in your lower deep abs and pelvis, and less leaking urine!

The added bonus of calming the nervous system is supremely beneficial and is a good reason to do the Pearl Pull-Ups™ daily for 5-10 breaths or 5-10 minutes. Just start. With practice, you will start to see this breathing become a natural part of what you do, how you move, and you can then build on the strength of this solid core of you.

Liberally and unapologetically take moments throughout your day to do quiet breathing. When you start to get riled up or have no patience left, take more deep breaths and repeat a word, such as "calm," "thank you," or "love," to bring you back to the present moment. I use "thank you" and say it multiple times a day when I am feeling overwhelmed, busy, or even if my mind just starts racing about my to-do list or worrying about my kids.

Saying "thank you" puts me into that immediate place of being grateful for what I have, who I am, and just for being alive. There is nothing simpler to bring peace back to yourself quickly than to realize how grateful you are to be living and breathing.

Start looking at your to-do list and rather than always adding things, start eliminating things. Start breathing throughout your day and focus not on how your body needs to change or how things in general should be different, but instead on how you are truly feeling inside and what you really need and want now.

Become aware of those little messages your body is trying to communicate to you. Maybe it's the nagging pain in your hip or your knee or a recurring headache. Maybe it's your abdomen growing without you noticing at all, like what happened to my friend Heather. Heather was so busy growing her business and being a mom to three boys that she didn't notice her belly growing for no reason. One day, she finally decided her abdomen looked like she was 6 months pregnant, it was time to get it checked out. Well, Heather went into the emergency room and didn't come out of the hospital until she had chemotherapy and cancer treatment for a rare and fast growing tumor that was about to take her life. You'll bet she started to take notice and started to heed her needs after that experience. Now she has used that experience to reflect on and tap into what her soul truly craves (and shares it on her inspiring podcast, Mom is in Control) rather than fitting into some societal ideal she didn't even realize she didn't want to buy into.

Maybe, like me, it is your lower back, or you are constantly feeling stressed, depressed, anxious, angry, or resentful. Do you have digestive issues or ongoing insomnia, even when you eat nourishing foods and have the chance to sleep? Start noticing and feeling what's deeper than your thoughts. Your body is speaking to you, and if you become quiet, you can hear it.

Once you start noticing the pains/discomforts in your physical body, start assessing the thoughts or triggers that bring them on. Are they always there? Start assessing these and making notes in your journal so you can increase your awareness. Are the thoughts in your head that are leading to physical and emotional pain really known facts? As the great author and teacher of self-inquiry Byron Katie discusses in *Loving What Is: Four Questions That Can Change Your Life*, "Who would you be without the thought?"

What if you say to yourself one or more of these statements? "I'm not good enough. I will never reach my goals. I have no support. I am too far gone. My baby never sleeps. I have no time. I've always been this way . . . "

Is that really true? Like *really* true? Can you be 100 percent sure that it's true?

If you can start to let go of those old, limiting beliefs and instead start to tell yourself something more encouraging, everything begins to change.

You will quickly see that a calmer, more open, patient, loving, and relaxed person start to appear when you don't put the pressure of old, belief systems—shoulds, coulds, will do, or "I'm not good enough unless . . . "—in front of yourself each day.

Start assessing what is your true current reality. Are you creating the things you don't want in your life by expecting them? Begin trusting that you have the power to change things through love and not through sheer force of will.

By allowing yourself to daydream, tune inward, be patient, live from gratitude, show reverence, and love yourself and the body you have right now, you can create a deep sense of peace from moment to moment, knowing that you are exactly where you are supposed to be. All that you want is available to you and will arrive, when you are open and allow it to flow in.

Because you can't control the sleeping schedule or the feeding schedule of your baby, because you can't control the needs of others, or your work and/or family/life schedules, what you can do is start to trust in the simple act of awareness that it isn't working for you. Only after calm reflection and assessment of your current reality can you start to create what it is you truly want.

This perspective shift is incredibly impactful. You will start seeing things from a different angle than when you were stuck under that big blanket of "shoulds."

When you start tuning in to and responding to feelings in your body (by breathing deeply, calming the mind, and listening), trusting it and acting on it, you start to get back to the beautiful art of self-care.

You can say, "Maybe this body that housed my babies and feeds them and does everything for the people around me is worthy of love."

You start to get back to that place you might not even remember having been before, where you have that inner trust and deep self-love that you were born with. You will start to realize that looking to others for their approval and asking what others are doing might not be "the way" for you.

You can forge your own path, and it all begins by honoring yourself and embracing the now. Then having the delicate discipline to keep acting moment to moment from that place of love.

This whole concept sounds simple, but by no means am I trying to convince you that it's easy. We have been conditioned for a long time to be the way we are, and we have done things a certain way and thought a certain way toward ourselves for a long, long time.

Commit to start listening to yourself and finding what you really need and want *now*, to what's your reality *now*, and what's realistic and good for you right *now*, in this moment, in this body, with these children, this job, with this partner, and with this current life situation. Don't think about what you wished for and don't spend time feeling bad about not being there.

When you keep practicing this new habit of turning inward instead of outward, that new perspective has the chance to become yours on a full-time basis. It becomes your automatic reaction to approach all things through self-love and not something you have to work toward.

At first, if it feels foreign to speak lovingly and kindly to yourself, you can start with talking to yourself, as you would speak to your best friend or loved one. Would you say the damaging things to them that you are saying to yourself? I would guess not.

I am sure you can relate to being your biggest critic and being harder on yourself than anyone else. I know I was. And this tendency still creeps in, to push myself, to say yes when I want to say no, or to hold myself to an impossible standard I would never hold another person to. Yes, we are often our own worst enemy in many ways, because we are not doing this, we could be doing that, we are shouting inside, we are wasting time on this, or we are letting ourselves down again.

When we keep reminding ourselves to speak as if this is our best friend we are looking at and speaking to, we start to say to her (ourselves), "Calm down, babe, you've got this! You look amazing! Look what you've been through and all that you're doing. Your body doesn't define you. I love you anyway, darling! Look at the circumstances you are working against. Look at how much sleep you've gotten. Look at what you are doing with your days; do you even have a spare moment? Look at all you are tending to. Look at all the amazing parts of your life and yourself, focus on that and just breathe. You've got this."

So, take time for calm, for connection, with yourself, for looking within every single day. We always think we're so busy that we could never fit a meditation practice into our day, or a twice-weekly workout class, or a yoga video, or a daily walk. But I know, even without knowing your personal schedule, that you do have time for breathing, for exercise, for anything you want. If you don't, please personally call or message me.

I want to talk to you about your specific situation, because I know you have time at least for breathing, calmly connecting to yourself, and meditating deep within daily.

Take action on your goals. My day planner, the *Passion Planner*, has a quote that I stuck on my computer: "Action cures fear" (David J. Schwartz).

I am so often asked by my clients or FitMamas online about this concept of fear of failure. They are so scared to fail that they don't even begin. And they then get stuck in a vicious cycle of feeling sub-par for far too long.

Begin by creating a vision of what you want, and then become aware of what in your current life situation is standing in your way. Then by breaking down your goals into small monthly, weekly, and more important, daily goals, you will start to take action by following through.

If you miss a day, a week, or a month here or there, trust that it isn't the end of the world. Your goals are not going to be ruined. Have patience from moment to moment with yourself and your body and believe in your body's innate wisdom. It grew your baby without you interfering, so aim not to interfere in its needs, just tune in and honor them.

Know that each little thing adds up to another. Know that each step you put in front of another adds up to this journey of your life being as perfect as it is meant to be. And yes, we take a few steps back here and there. Maybe more than we like at some times of the year or some times in our lives. But the reality is, we have to set that intention and keep an eye on the prize: how do we want to look and feel 50 years from now? This is about aligning with that vision for yourself and taking daily action nurturing yourself with love and patience along the way.

FITMAMA FOUNDATION: Your body hears everything that your mind says to it.

"Self-talk" has become more of a buzzword recently, whereas 30 years ago this concept of the voice in your head was rarely talked about (except maybe with respect to mental disorders). As we have evolved, we have come to realize that everyone has this voice in their heads, known as the "ego," "imposter," "gatekeeper," etc. This voice keeps you stuck in fear and low self-worth.

Beginning a simple practice of awareness about your thoughts will allow you to see where the words you are speaking within yourself are holding you back or keeping you stuck. It comes back to the old, ingrained patterns that you've repeated so often that they have become who you are.

Affirmations can be a good way of planting seeds in your head. The great Louise Hay's motivational work in *You Can Heal Your Life* shares how these affirmations can deeply change the course of healing from trauma—physically, mentally, emotionally, and spiritually. Affirmations allow you to plant seeds in your mind of what you WANT, instead of what you don't want. You can begin to live your days in a way that make you feel connected to who you truly are beneath all the stories.

Find within yourself a daily affirmation that works with the idea that patience is to be cultivated day in and day out. Listen to that inner knowing that says to you, "You are exactly where you need to be." So, say out loud to yourself every morning when you wake up, and every night when you go to bed, "I am exactly where I need to be."

Speak honestly and deeply to your subconscious mind, which you can only reach when you are in that place of calmer beta waves, alpha waves, and theta waves. Calm your nervous system, slow the brain chatter, deeply breathe, and connect to your breath in this moment. Look, listen, and trust.

FITMAMA FOUNDATION: You are exactly where you need to be.

The Persian adage, "This too shall pass" (both the good and the not so good), is something you can say to yourself to calm yourself as you take time daily to breathe through the fear.

Immediately when something triggers you that you feel out of control of, that you feel frustrated by, or feel like you can't handle, start connecting to your breath, which will naturally slow your nervous system and calm your brain wave activity. Then, from that place, trust that you CAN handle all that is coming your way. When triggered, pair your breath with that trigger, the way Russian physiologist Ivan Pavlov trained his dogs with classical conditioning. Repetition.

Breathe. Repeat.

Just stop and take deep breaths, knowing that letting go of control is what will lead to your desired outcomes, not the opposite.

Become more present in your current reality. Fear, anxiety, and depression come from being stuck in worry about past and future uncontrollables.

I remember when I first had my oldest daughter. For the first six weeks, I was in absolute awe. I was in complete shock, and I was on a literal high like no other that I could recall in my whole life, where I just felt absolutely incredible. I was so proud of myself, I was so pleased that I was healthy, that my baby was healthy, and we could return to life as we knew it. I could get back to doing things that I couldn't do when I was pregnant—maybe drinking some wine, maybe going places that I didn't have the energy to go while I was pregnant.

The whole time I was able to take my little one out with me, I used to joke that she was the best little accessory, that she just went with everything and was so cute and made me feel amazing everywhere I went. And at the same time as I felt happy and excited with these blissful feelings, there was this intense "pit in my stomach" feeling all the time that I was on the clock, that I was in a rush.

Because I was breastfeeding, I was the sole provider of her food and this felt stressful at times. She wasn't keen on taking a bottle, and my body wasn't keen on pumping, so it was one of those situations where we seemed glued at the hip and every time she needed to feed, I was there. The feeling of wanting some alone time was there for me. I also had a lot of doubt in myself, whether I was spending enough time doing this or that, or should I do this instead? I remember justifying a lot to myself, instead of just being.

First Thought Technique

Throughout my many years of postsecondary education; trainings; books; certifications; and years in the health, nutrition, and fitness industry, I came across almost NO information about tuning inward and trusting your gut. Listening to your body and understanding its cues was a lesser-known art in fitness, because the fitness world has got such a "no pain, no gain" mentality that leaves us disassociating from our body's cues to "keep on pushing."

A few years ago, one of my mentors taught me a skill that has proven to be incredibly valuable for my clients and me. It's called the "first thought technique," and I teach it now as a part of my FitMama Foundations. As I mentioned before, we think we love following a plan, but plans are not worth more than the paper they are written on. Life happens, especially after babies.

We have two sides to our brain, the left and the right. The left side is the logical, thinking, analytical side that is always trying to reason with us and justify things, "You should do the laundry, because there are only 30 minutes until she wakes again." "You didn't work out yesterday, so don't nap, as you have to work out today." But it doesn't take into account what we really want, and what our subconscious selves want. We probably do not want to do the laundry and we need to nap, but we don't even give ourselves that option.

The idea behind the first thought technique is that your right brain, your nonlogical, present awareness, intuitive side of the brain usually gets usurped by the left brain thoughts.

Science has found, though, that the right brain comes to decisions quicker, because it doesn't have to go through the logic that the left brain does. To that end, if we ask ourselves a question, such as, "There are only 30 minutes until the baby wakes; do you want to do laundry or take a nap?" we then pause.

Listen closely to the first thought that comes in. Slow down when listening and tune into what your body is saying. Maybe your first thought is laundry and you go do it, but if the first thought is a nap, then you go do that. What feels like a weight lifted off your body? Your first thought technique and tuning into your visceral reactions to these first thoughts, all your answers will come.

The key is to honor your first thought and follow through. This tells your right brain, "Yes, I am going to listen and trust you more."

Our logic fails us. It is most often so clouded by judgment, misinformation, negative emotions from the past, expectations, and more. This first thought technique allows you, though, to ask your true self questions, and see what you have to say.

The key with this concept is honoring and practicing it often. When out for a walk, say, "Should I turn right or left?" If your first thought is left, go left. At dinner, if you are deciding between broccoli and spinach, ask which one and honor what the first thought says.

This has become so valuable a technique for me and so many others. It just allows you to let go of the pressure and honor the you inside.

I so wish I had this tool earlier in life, where I would logic my way into so many situations that I didn't need to be part of.

I think this would have helped me cut down on my self-doubt and even more cut down on my rushing, always trying to be the perfect mom, wife, homemaker, trainer, coach, and more.

I recall the only times I would really feel that feeling of having some time to myself were those moments when I would just have fed my daughter, and she would go to sleep maybe, or I would run out to the store and she would be with my husband. I would have those moments where I could just be breathing deeper, and I wouldn't be on the clock. I found that I would almost be hyperventilating in my breath. I would feel almost shaky with everything I was doing. I was going so full-speed ahead to fit it all in. There was no patience in my frantic rushing back then. If I put her down for a nap, I would be like, "Oh! I might just only have an hour so, so I had better do this, this, this, and this, before she wakes up." And I felt more of this in response: *rush, rush, rush.*

This is still something that I work on with myself, but now I use this tool to prioritize. I love to fit as many things into my days as I can, and you may try to do this too. But this can lead to breakdowns in self-care—and then we get triggered back into those old habit patterns that we are trying to get out of.

Mel Robbins has tapped into the latest research around getting yourself to do things that are best for you or as I say to my clients, "The habits that are aligned with who you want to be." In her book, *The 5 Second Rule*, Mel talks about how counting down backwards from 5 (4, 3, 2, 1) and then taking action, just one step towards what you are resisting (getting out of bed and not pushing snooze, going to that early workout class or pushing through easy to eat healthier) makes you do things over time that you thought impossible. It's a fine balance with pushing yourself and easing off. Trust your gut (intuition) and use the first thought technique to guide you in your choices. Our lives are a series of little decisions all day long that dictate how we act. Our repeated actions (or inactions) dictate our habits and truly become our life. Lifestyle Medicine is a newer area of medicine that takes a holistic approach to our mind and body health. Research shows that our lifestyle has a massive impact on our long term health and well being. It's an understatement, and it's an understatement to say that what we do and think each day of our lives plays a role in our overall health and longevity. It's everything, really.

The tools that have really helped me, and so many of my clients are based on the latest research. Taking deep breaths often throughout the day and setting my alarm as a reminder throughout the day to take a moment to connect within have been highly beneficial to developing the overall calm and presence that forms the foundations of healthy lifestyle habits. Deeply calming the nervous system allows us to start to feel like everything will get done in good time. Because of course, it will.

LOVE FITMAMA CHAPTER TAKEAWAY

1. Take time daily to practice the "first thought technique."

2. Break big goals into smaller, more realistic, and attainable goals and you can get more "wins."

3. Daily spend time reminding and affirming, "This too shall pass," to remind you to just breathe through it.

CHAPTER 3

Presence: Let Go to Grow

"Your children need your presence more than your presents."

—Jesse Jackson

When I was 10 weeks pregnant with my first daughter, I had the opportunity to go on a 10-day silent meditation retreat, my official introduction to the practice of Vipassana meditation. I was in the first few years of starting my business, when a friend suggested we go together. Having just found out I was pregnant the month before, it was starting to sink in how little freedom I'd actually have to do things like this on a whim once the baby arrived. I was open to a challenge and welcomed the change in scenery.

Because I had read extensively on the benefits of meditation and had been practicing it a little on my own, I was curious. Being away and spending 12 hours a day meditating was an eye-opening experience, to say the least. During this 10 days of silence, we weren't allowed to make eye contact with others or smile or gesture. We weren't allowed to read or to write or to do anything else for the 10 days either. Our entire purpose was to just BE—alone with ourselves, our hearts, and our breath.

Researchers have been studying our brain wave activity for years, and they demonstrate clearly that we are in a fight-or-flight response neurochemically for a lot of our waking hours. The HeartMath Institute in California has demonstrated, through collating many studies on the matters of heart coherence, that the electrical and magnetic forces within and around the heart have a significant connection to emotions.

By intentionally focusing on positive emotions, and generating a more consistent state of "heart coherence," individuals have demonstrated healthier brain and body functions at the individual and social levels. The studies show the interconnectedness of emotions between humans and their work displays our oneness with other humans, all living beings, and all things we can and cannot see in our environments and within us.

By connecting to this heart coherent state throughout the day, we can cultivate that calm, connected clarity that comes from being present and aware. Like we would be if we were all of a sudden to find ourselves alone with a large bear.

This presence model represents the connection between the now and the past and future to reach a fully present state.

It's inevitable that we speak about the past, think about the past, and it's inevitable that we worry about the future. We are designed for survival, such that we've evolved to think controlling things will help our survival, so we try to plan or control how things will turn out. The place we find ourselves least, ironically, is the present moment. Finding harmony with these three mind frames, in a way that allows us to be in that space of calm presence as we go through our days, is attainable, with action.

The first step is to let go of anything that's happened in the past. Are you holding a grudge? Holding grudges is one of the things you will regret most as you grow older. Let anything go that you feel isn't serving you anymore, it's not worth carrying the pain.

My back serves as a sign for me in situations like this. Grudges, anger, resentment, exhaustion, overwhelm, and other heavy emotions can burden us and feel heavy on our bodies. My back aches and stabs me when I get too tired, or when I agree to something I really want to say no to. I have a system now to breathe through these moments of resistance and realize that I have a choice, and I can choose to take action *for* myself instead of *against* myself. Anger, resentment, and grudges most especially go against ourselves, the person on the receiving end feels much less emotional pain than us and might even be oblivious. This can just bring up more pain within us.

Now is the time to let it go. Having a child can often bring up things from our own childhood that we might have covered up, not thought about, or not wanted to think about as they were too painful or just not memorable. So, let things go. It's not about adding it all up and justifying crappy behavior by saying, "Well, I do this because so and so did this to me." That doesn't matter right now. You want to let these things go, so you can stop reacting to them. As they come up, face them, journal about them, sort out the details of them, and realize that they don't affect your life anymore. It's YOU, FitMama, who's suffering.

When it comes to the now, just breathe, just be there, and breathe in daily. The breath is the best tool you have. It's with you everywhere you go, and it takes control of itself due to the situation that you are in. If, all of a sudden something scares you, you can find yourself starting to breathe heavier, faster, shorter or you may hold your breath. But you have the ability to control that by telling yourself this is not something to get worked up over. Just breathe—long, deep, and slow.

With regard to the future, don't try to control everything: just be curious. Create that level of curiosity that allows you to open your mind, and be open to the opportunities that come to teach you as your life unfolds. Avoid trying to control.

And when you can balance this past, future, and now, you start to open your mind, you start to own your story, and you start to get into that space of opportunity to find, see, be, and do all the things that the moment allows. That moment can only be allowed when it isn't clouded with the past or the future. Breathe into that moment to get to the calm presence at the center of it all, that calm presence that comes from owning your story, from being open-minded, and from looking at obstacles as opportunities to learn, grow, and evolve, to become more conscious, and to become a brighter light in your life.

FITMAMA FOUNDATION: Each day take action toward shedding old stories that hold you back.

When it comes to deciding what or how to move forward, while taking a calmer and more present approach to your self-care and fitness goals, it requires a few key elements that you will find to be useful in all areas of life.

Each moment seemed LONG while I was at the meditation center. The first three days were the longest. Then they seemed to speed up a little. I started seeing each moment as an opportunity. A chance to really be aware of time and to see the things happening around me and within me. The magic of meditation lies in the disconnecting from what you think is you, to what really IS you. Just empty space. Just energy and spirit. Just love. Just a beautiful soul who can choose how she wants to use this one opportunity at life.

Awareness

Listen and watch closely to what is actually happening in your life. Start to write these "stories" that you are telling yourself all the time, the stories that author Brené Brown calls "SFDs" or "shitty first drafts." She also points out that confronting people or things with this line preceding what you say can really make an impact— on others and yourself: "The story I am telling myself is . . . "

We tell ourselves stories all day long. We drain our own energy and take away our own power. So often we cloud our own judgment based on experiences and our versions of how they went. We forget that in each moment we have the option to choose our perspective. These negative repetitive thought patterns turn into our way of life. It is our *"personality* that creates our *personal reality,"* as Dr. Joe Dispenza says in his book, *Breaking the Habit of Being Yourself.* All we see is more of what we don't want, unless we approach it with a new mind and become that different person.

Judgment is universal in the mom world, especially in the fit-mom world. We negatively judge another to make ourselves feel better, or we positively judge them and compare ourselves and then feel worse. Either way, it's a useless exercise that doesn't bring happiness or contentment. We can stop judging one another, because truly we are only judging ourselves. So, tune in, listen, and watch closely to what is actually happening inside you, where you don't come at it from a place of fear or judgment or creating self-fulfilling prophecies where they aren't needing to be fulfilled. Just listen and watch what's really happening, to what people are really saying, not to what you interpret them as saying.

Disconnect

Turn off all devices and distractions for at least a few hours per day. More is better. Yes, we all have needs and desires with regard to our phones, whether it's the camera, whether it's communication with others, or if it's connecting with others at some level. But ultimately, it's through these three things that we tend to truly *lose connection* with what really matters, and often that's what is right in front of us NOW.

So, have a plan with your partner that for at least one to three hours a day, the phones are put away in another room with sounds off. You are setting boundaries for yourself to create connection with the community you want most to be connected to—your partner and children. And regardless of what excuses you might have regarding your job or what needs you have with the phone, trust that you can live without it for at least a few hours a day, and be truly present with and for those you love. Starting with YOU. Tune inward.

Be Here Now

Start to notice your thoughts and whether you are thinking of things in the past or in the future. Notice if you are getting back into that space of wishing things were different than they are, hoping that if you do this one thing that everything is going to change. Notice if you are wanting to control the future and not being ready to let go of the past, not being ready to be curious about the future will keep you stuck.

If you are doing that, it can be a trigger for you to affirm to yourself something like, "Be here now." Every moment when you get into that thinking about the past or thinking about the future, trying to control or trying to redo the past in your mind so it doesn't look as bad as you think it did, is just a waste of time and energy. Say to yourself, "I am here now" and know that this moment is the only one that matters, that in this moment nothing can be wrong. This is the moment for you to *be here now.*

So, breathe into your heart, think of things that move you to love, feel those feelings of true love and joy that you had when you first held your newborn baby, those feelings of love and joy when your dreams as you imagined them became reality. Breathe into your heart space, calm your mind, expand your heart, and live daily from that place of love.

LOVE FITMAMA CHAPTER TAKEAWAY

4. Find harmony by owning your choices. Your past doesn't dictate your future, unless you let it.

5. Open your mind to what the future might bring. Don't try to predict it.

6. See the opportunity in each moment to be present and connect with what's actually happening right now.

CHAPTER 4

Permission: Laugh with Life

*"When you are brave enough to be yourself,
you give others permission to do the same."*

—Unknown

Giving yourself permission to be you can be a most powerful, life-changing experience. This is something I learned early on from my younger, but much wiser, sister, Alex. I lived with her in Vancouver during the summer of 2004, and we had such a great time together. I remember this was at a time in my life where I was constantly wanting to be better and looking at myself externally as a person, wanting to know what I could do to be better and on and on and on (okay, sometimes I am still this way, I will admit). So, I was still working to that point where I was okay with who I was. And I used to always say, "Oh, I wish I was this way," or "I should be this way more."

And my little sister wisely said to me, "Just be who you are! Just be okay with the fact that this is who you are. Don't try to be anyone else." And this, though it seems to be quite a simple concept, is a lesson I still needed to learn more than a decade later (insert cringe). We can get on that hamster wheel and run, run, run after that idea that we should be constantly striving to be a better, more socially acceptable, different version of ourselves. But like the hamster, we don't see that for all our running, we are still in the same place.

Give yourself permission to just be, to just be you. To be in this moment, to not judge yourself, to not tell yourself you should be this way or that way, or things should be some other way, or something should be this way or that way. Just be. Why do we wait for someone to give us this permission? We can grant it to ourselves.

To that end, it was only just recently that I really fully GOT this, after I hurt myself and couldn't be active in the way that represented me. Was that me? The me who could lift heavy, run far, and beat people in competitions? Or was this me? The me who couldn't bend or move without pain? The answer is BOTH. It's an ever-changing, moment-to-moment fluid thing, this thing I call ME.

Recently I was reminded of this again, when I needed it from my business mentors who said, "It's about being more OF yourself, not about being more THAN yourself."

A more evolved version of ourselves is available moment to moment, and it's just about staying aware and being the best version of who we are right now, while unconditionally LOVING who we are right now. This allows us the space and nurturing we need to grow as humans.

I was only truly able to receive the permission notice when I realized that I didn't need to be good at everything, or the best at everything, as I was so competitively programmed to expect from myself in my athlete, warrior mentality. I could just be me, and that was enough.

One of the forerunners in this area of research is professor Brené Brown, who does lots of work on vulnerability. In her book, *Rising Strong: How the Ability to Reset Transforms the Way We Live, Love, Parent, and Lead,* she discusses this idea that we are always trying to be these versions of ourselves who are not really us, but these versions that we put out into the world to try to be better, stronger, etc., than we think we are. I want to go further into the research in vulnerability in this area, which is going to be specific to this idea of giving yourself permission.

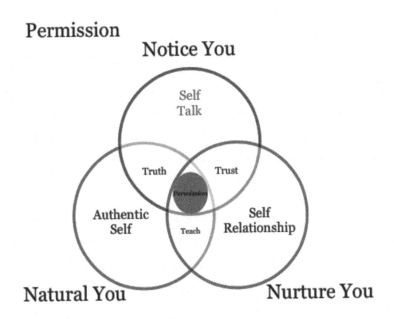

This permission model that I created is about three details of you. It's about noticing yourself, nurturing yourself, and being your natural self. Because until we really notice ourselves and notice the things we say, do, and think all day, we aren't coming from a perspective of wisdom. We don't notice the things we are saying to ourselves or how they are affecting us in different, possibly negative ways. We are just going through the motions of life and not taking a moment to reflect.

Notice Yourself

The first step to giving yourself permission is to notice yourself. Journaling is something I recommend doing on a daily basis. To start to notice yourself, to notice the things you are thinking about and saying, it's simple to reflect them in a journaling session, rather than just think about them.

Often, I find myself spending time with people due to various circumstances in my life, and having conversations with them and agreeing with them about things that I don't truly believe or am not truly thinking about at this time. Maybe it's something that I thought in the past, maybe it's a reflection of something I thought I was meant to think or know, but it doesn't reflect me anymore.

We can often be around others and find ourselves thinking like someone we are really not, maybe someone we once were when we knew them, and old ways creep in. So, start to notice you and your self-talk and notice where that self-talk came from, for example, "I am saying this to myself, and it's funny because my mom always said that to herself."

Nurture Yourself

If you don't focus on you, nurture yourself, and attend to your needs, nobody else will. Nobody else is going to take care of you, if you don't. You know that. And that's not a "Oh, woe is me" statement, that's a fact. We teach others how to treat us. If we treat ourselves with disrespect, others will treat us with disrespect.

So, we always need to treat ourselves with absolute, unconditional, pure, beautiful, white-light, reverence love. You can cultivate this relationship with yourself where you—yes, you—hold yourself to a high standard, not to look down on other people but to hold yourself to a standard where you know you come from love, you are love, and you show love. The only way to do that is by showing yourself love and by nurturing yourself through daily practices that honor yourself.

Your Natural Self

Starting to explore who you are at your core, when you're not being influenced by others, is a vital piece in the permission process. Explore that authentic self who you are behind closed doors, that quality of a person who you are deep down, underneath everything else. Look underneath those layers of socialization, interpretation, expectations, and what we were told had to be, underneath our families, upbringings, cultures, idealizations, religious beliefs, or whatever it is that we were taught and might no longer be serving us.

That natural and authentic you is underneath it all. Start to chisel away with all your might to get deeper, to the higher, true, inner you. Because once you notice you, and you nurture you, you can start to create a more authentic relationship with yourself.

Trust Starts with You

Do you trust yourself? I know it sounds like it should be an obvious answer, but actually in most cases, we don't trust ourselves. We create this mistrust when you tell yourself you are going to start a diet on Monday and then you don't start. Or you tell yourself you are going to eat better, or do X, Y, and Z for yourself and you don't. This creates a deep rift within yourself. When you start to notice your self-talk and the relationship it has with your true self, you can start to trust. You start to get further down into that natural you, finding the deeper truths that lie under the talk that's been distracting you all this time.

When you get to that natural you, that authentic self, and you are cultivating that deep connection with you and that self-relationship, you start to teach yourself and teach those around you how it is to treat you. You teach others how to interact with you, what expectations they should have when they come to meet you. This is a place of humble, unconditional love for you and reverence for all around you in your life. It starts to come to the surface and build to the center point of permission for you to be and do and have whatever it is that you know you truly deserve.

By giving yourself this permission, you can take the next step to create the routines in your life that cultivate your authentic self: taking that time for you, talking to others in a certain way that helps build this respect and trust that you will get the job done when you say you will.

When you say there is time for you in every day that you will take for you and your needs, you're really serious and you don't give that up for anyone or anything. And when shit hits the fan, it gets bigger and it gets deeper. You double and triple and quadruple the you time, because that's when you need it most. Only you can give yourself permission. Only you can choose to never feel judged by another. Only you make yourself feel guilty, wrong, or bad. It's all up to you.

Find Your Gratitude

Every day, write five to ten things you are grateful for.

The research on this practice is incredible. If you can write something, even one thing, every day that you are grateful for, I guarantee you will start to look around your world during the day to find things that you are grateful for to put on your list that night. Every night before going to bed, write things that you are grateful for that day, and then every morning you are waking up and looking for things you are grateful for during the day. You will start to create a beautiful, virtuous cycle of love, reverence, peace, joy, happiness, and bliss, for the little things in life. You connect the dots, creating the pieces of the life you are here to live.

Find Your Self-Love

Every day, write five to ten things that you love about yourself.

Yes, you should be able to find five to ten things that you love about yourself every single day. Not things like "I love my hair, or I love my purse I bought." Choose deep core elements that you love about yourself. It can be the same ten things from yesterday, but every day you should have this conversation with yourself.

- I love myself because of this . . .

- I love myself because I truly love others, because I smile at the world, regardless of how it looks back at me.

- I love myself and my family.

- I love myself because I was open to the teaching that my mom had for me about dreaming in technicolor daily.

- I love myself because I love others.

- I love myself because I naturally want to help those around me.

- I love myself because I can see beauty in everyone I meet.

- I love myself because I can see to the core of a person and not what is on the outside.

- I love myself because I breathe deeply every day.

- I love myself because I listen to what my needs are.

- I love myself because I truly trust myself, because I know I can conquer anything.

- I love myself because it's not me who dictates everything about me. It's God, and I let go and let God (or whatever higher power you believe in).

Find Your Triggers

Write three triggers that you notice cause you to start to be someone you are not.

This is for when you notice yourself starting to go down the path of self-loathing, of self-disrespect, or of self-deprecation. Maybe you think it's in good humor, but what are you really saying to yourself every time you look into the mirror and say you need to change? What are you doing to yourself when you tell yourself you're not good enough, deserving enough, or special enough to have something in your life? Your trigger is like an alarm bell, a red alert going off in your mind that then flips that switch and you have a different conversation in your mind.

For me, when I am tired, overworked or prepping for a video or presentation, I see myself picking myself apart and feeling like I need to change. My hair, my clothes, my makeup. My habits, routines, my life direction. When I feel rested these things don't show up. When I haven't seen my kids in a few days because of work travel, it triggers me to worry, feel like a bad mom or feel like I am not there for them. It naturally spirals downhill and I feel continually worse and worse. When I connect with my values and trust my path, these don't show up. Often we need to just get out of our own way. Get out of our own heads. Get back into our core. The core of our being. What our journey here on earth is really about.

I imagine, what can I put my energy into right now? Who needs me right now? What if I am sitting here worrying about my hair color or my toes or my belly flab or whatever else I am worrying about, and there is someone out there who needs me to put my energy into something better?

Who can I help who is less fortunate than me? Who needs me right now who I can show my love to and share my passion for helping others with that will then shift my perspective away from myself and all my flaws, which I will inevitably find more of the longer I look in the mirror.

It's a useless task that I don't want any part of in my life, or in yours. So, start to look at your own life and what your triggers are that cause you to start looking or feeling a certain way. Because once you find them, you can start to change those patterns, those pathways, and rewire your brain in this new way.

LOVE FITMAMA CHAPTER TAKEAWAY

1. Journal often and notice your self-talk and how it affects your feelings and behaviors.

2. Nurture the relationship with yourself by taking time and energy for you. Journaling is a fabulous tool.

3. Be the natural you who is underneath all the social masks you wear.

Part 2

Nurture: Heal Your Seal

CHAPTER 5

Retrain to Rewire

"For fast-acting relief, try slowing down."

—Lily Tomlin

The one thing a woman needs most right after she has a baby: rest.

The one thing a woman is unlikely to get any of right after she has a baby: rest.

The thing is, though, this usually isn't because the baby is up all the time. That will be the reason for mom not getting sleep, but rest is a different story.

Rest is something that we seldom allow ourselves, even after giving birth.

I remember the year my oldest was born, it was Good Friday that she decided to come into this world, right on her due date, April 22. My water broke at 5:00 a.m., and I called my mom to come to Windsor. She was in Hamilton, about a three-hour drive. She was right to assume that first births are never fast, so she took her sweet time packing and heading over.

As you now know, I like to go against the grain. By the time I got some cramping it was 7:00 a.m. Then I decided to go to the hospital, because I couldn't stand it anymore and I had the urge to push. I got to the hospital, walked up to my room, and in less than an hour from check in, I was holding my sweet baby girl.

Yes, my mom missed it.

She arrived about 30 minutes later. The baby and I were good, so we were released shortly after the birth. We got home about 3:00 p.m., after having only left my house at 9:30 that morning to go to the hospital, so I felt like I had just gone to the store, picked up a baby, and came home. Yes, I have a horseshoe up my butt (as my parents would say, as I am born on St. Patty's Day and the luck of the Irish always finds me). Other than staying calmly open and curious to how the birth would go, I am not saying it was anything I did per se to have a quick birth.

In the warrior mindset that I lived in then, I was like "Oh, well that was just a blip on the radar, back to it!" So, even that day I came home, yes, I sat mostly and rested a bit, but my whole family was present. My siblings came from Toronto to meet my little one and, because it was Good Friday, they all had the weekend off. While they stayed in a hotel and I, by no means, was not standing up cooking, I was still getting up and down, grabbing stuff for people, walking around and taking the stairs multiple times daily.

Looking back, this makes me cringe, knowing the pelvic floor like I do now, but, at the time, that was my norm. I was not feeling my body and was just being in my head about what it could do. Resting wasn't even on my radar, as I had such a high feeling after having the baby. I didn't give it another thought. It felt so good, after all, to not be pregnant. I loved being pregnant, but I had forgotten how good it felt to just carry one body around!

Now, I teach birth, then breathe.

Oh, the Core, a Bore No More

When women are pregnant, due to the growing baby, the pressure inside our abdomens increases. This is called intra-abdominal pressure (IAP). Because of the increased IAP during pregnancy, our breathing patterns change. Instead of following the natural breathing flow of expanding and contracting the pelvic floor, diaphragm, transversus abdominis, and multifidus synergistically to proper core function, the IAP contributes to a change in the way we relax and contract that can cause core dysfunction and the many negative symptoms associated.

It's natural for us to want to tend to everyone right after we have a baby, because we feel like "I don't have this extra 20 pounds around my belly anymore; it's not so uncomfortable; and don't I feel energized, fabulous, and just want to move, move, move, move. That was me anyway, and many others I speak to. And so, it's easy to get into that mentality.

However, the most important things to do after having a baby are exactly this—*rest, rehab,* and *routine.* By rest, I mean actually not going anywhere or doing anything. People love going to the mall and going grocery shopping, but doing this requires you to stand and that puts pressure and pushes all your organs down onto your pelvic floor while it is still supremely traumatized, weak, and fragile after the birth. After all, you pushed a baby out of there! It doesn't matter how fit or strong you are, you still need *time* to recover. So, if you don't rest and take the pressure off your body, it's constantly being forced to work, and hold up all those organs as they begin to shift back into place.

This can lead to pain and physical strain. Especially if, at that time when your pelvic floor is weakest after birth and you're standing up, you sneeze or cough. Ouch! Downward pressure. And every time you cough, it puts even more downward pressure onto your pelvic floor—and so, please, please, PLEASE, stay off your feet for as long as you can. And sit to cough and sneeze for at least a few months.

As you learn to contract, relax, and retrain your body to breathe correctly through core breathing, Pearl Pull-Ups™, and the many other exercises taught at FitMama, you more naturally will strengthen and relax the pelvic floor and the muscles around your urethra, your vagina where you birthed your baby, and, of course, your anus. The whole pelvic floor is comprised of these.

Performing the simple daily act of breathing, in a core concentrated way, absolutely 100 percent will support your entire body and mind. Taking time to deeply breathe every day not only works to relax you and calm the nervous system, but it retrains your deep inner core and pelvic floor region to move safely and properly and recoordinates the proper form and function of your diaphragm and pelvic floor with your transversus abdominis (TVA) and multifidus before internal and external obliques and rectus abdominis (the outer muscles) even get involved.

So, the deep inner core is the pelvic floor, the TVA, the multifidus, and the diaphragm; your breathing muscle. The inner and outer obliques and the rectus abdominis are the larger, external (or superficial, in anatomy speak) stabilizing muscles, which you don't want to be engaging with ab work until the deep muscles are retrained and strong enough.

By starting with Pearl Pull-Ups™ and core breathing, you will strengthen the inner unit, so you aren't using those larger, external muscles to stabilize the core and ending up with a weak, inner core where you tend to laugh and leak, or sneeze and leak.

FITMAMA FOUNDATION: Stay flat for five.

What I mean by that is staying flat (sitting or lying) on one level of your house or dwelling and NOT taking the stairs for a minimum of five days. I get crazy responses when I suggest this, and even the most conscientious FitMamas will say, "I will try," which we all know means, "I will not do it, but it will cross my mind while I am taking the stairs."

"Do. Or do not. There is no try," as the famous Yoda quote goes from *The Empire Strikes Back*.

What I say is if you can heed this advice, you are giving your pelvic floor a lifelong gift. If you can manage avoiding stairs more than one to two times per day for 7–10 days, then even better.

Go upstairs once, get what you need, stay up there for the day, and come down later for bed or vice versa. Go downstairs, stay down there for the whole day, and then go back up at the end of the day. Taking the pressure off your pelvic floor is of number one importance after giving birth. Stairs split your pelvic floor and add incredible pressure. Yes, this goes for C-section FitMamas too.

It's a must to rest that pelvic floor and let it recover. The first 8–10 weeks are the most critical time for recovery, so if you can do as little as possible in the way of putting pressure on your pelvic floor during that time, it will contribute to reduced incontinence and the lower likelihood of a prolapsed uterus postpartum.

In addition to avoiding too much activity postpartum, the most important recommendation I can make is going to see a pelvic floor physiotherapist and doing a targeted core rehabilitation protocol (there's more on this later in this book).

If you spend those 8–10 weeks rehabbing your pelvic floor safely while resting, you have the potential to have a stronger, more functional core postpartum than you have ever had before.

By doing this, you are taking conscious action to strengthen, retrain, and support your pelvic floor. This positively impacts the deep core unit by not causing more pressure.

The other deep core muscles get affected in the natural, rhythmic breathing nature they once knew, before all that IAP from housing and birthing your baby. Your entire body is affected when you're giving birth.

This recovery process requires going to that place of rest and rehabilitation and creating routines that feel good—realistic, not rigid routines, but safe, grounding, and energizing.

One of the most important suggestions I can make for you is if you haven't already done so, see a pelvic floor physiotherapist (PT) as soon as possible (unless you are pregnant and it's contraindicated for you, or if you are fewer than six weeks postpartum). This health professional is likely to do an internal exam, so if you are pregnant, get clearance from your doctor. I recommend this to 100 percent of FitMamas.

The PT will go internally with his or her hands, or possibly an ultrasound machine, to check the pelvic floor, muscles, ligaments, and pelvic region, so you are able to have a basis of understanding of what's going/gone on there, what trauma your body actually endured, and how to get it back to a place where it is stronger than before, which is where you want to be. A pelvic health/pelvic floor PT is going to get you there.

Give yourself a time frame from your birth or from now that you will give yourself permission to rest, rehab and heal with no pressure of going hard on your body. Give yourself three months, six months, three years, or whatever you think you can handle to start then keep assessing. Only then can you enter that space, take that time, and retrain without forcing. It's vital you give yourself the permission, have the patience, and cultivate the presence to just allow what is meant to happen during that time.

As you strengthen in both mind and body, you start to notice that this retraining process goes on, and you build on it like that gorgeous dream house you build for your family—except this one is your dream body. Not one that is perfect, as there is no perfection. Just this body of yours that you love and cherish.

Slowing, resting, and retraining is really the most vital part. After having a baby, you CAN be stronger in your core and pelvic floor than you were before. But take it from me, who hurt my back trying to keep pushing through pain because I wanted to exercise, it's not worth it. Much like a grade 4 pelvic organ prolapse (POP), back pain has a way of really taking over your life and demanding attention.

A grade 4 prolapse is when one of your pelvic organs is literally coming out of your vagina. This is a real possibility for us, if we don't rehab postpartum or take care of our deep inner core unit so it is functional.

I got the stabbing back pain wakeup call in 2014, after I was NOT embracing that my back was sore from a weak core I didn't know how to rehab at the time, and I was teaching multiple fitness classes and training clients.

Neglecting your body just means it stops working after a while, and you cannot neglect yourself anymore when you end up in the hospital twice in one week and literally cannot move. Life is calling—will you answer? Will you heed your needs before it's too late?

At the time when this was happening for me, I had a one year old and a three year old at home, I was still breastfeeding, and my husband was traveling extensively for work. I got stuck in a lot of chairs in those days and gritted my teeth in pain so I could get through the day. My back was hurting and I didn't heed my needs. I did this to myself.

I decided to see a chiropractor, who gave me an SI joint belt that I wore once and it forever changed my life. I wanted it to be the panacea that allowed me to keep working out.. I am sure you can think of times in your life like that. Were there signs to stop and you kept pushing? When did you push yourself too far?

This is an important point to remember: It's not about taking anything away from you. Like me, your workout regimen might be your point of sanity, your touchstone, or your grounding force. I am here to suggest to you that you can find other ways to feel sane or grounded, which don't require hurting yourself in the process.

It is about rebuilding that foundation of your body from the ground up and preserving your ability to do active things in your life later on, once you've recovered. Birthing is NOT a blip on the radar, no matter which way you look at it. When you rest, rehab, and create new routines around doing so, you are nurturing yourself—Your body, this day.

When you are resting and retraining, you reinforce that strong pelvic floor. You are starting to reinforce breathing in the correct way by concentrated breathing, at first, and then allowing it to naturally take over subconsciously with time. You're rewiring the brain and body pathways consciously through focused effort. Due to neuroplasticity, our brains are forever forming new connections. These new connections will serve to be the foundation of your strongest core yet.

Nurture Your Core

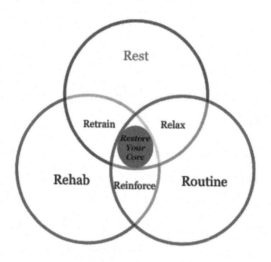

When you rehab and create routines to take care of yourself, you reinforce the rebuilding process. When you have create new routines, and you take rest regularly, then you start to relax, knowing that you are doing just what you need to do to get your body to the place where it's feeling better. When you rest and rehab you retrain the muscles and your whole body really for this new way of being. Your new role as mom. This begins when you put everything down and just breathe. Then allow yourself to decide what lifestyle habits and routine serve your highest good—mentally, emotionally, and physically.

So, in the center of that, you are truly restoring your core. This is where the core transformation begins—deep within.

And because of the nature of rest, rehab, and routine—just the act of cultivating those habits—you will start to notice the development of presence and permission. You start the growth of open-mindedness and owning your story, listening, trusting, and becoming that truer essence of you. Often, we say, "You can't teach an old dog new tricks," but neuroscience and psychology have now shown that it's never too late to teach an old dog new tricks. Rest, rehabilitation, and routine is all about healing your seal. It's as if you were playing basketball and you blew out your knee, and then the next day you decided that even though it only feels okay and mostly unstable and weak, you decide to keep training for the marathon next month anyway. It sounds crazy doesn't it?

Instead, you can take the time to rest, rebuild, and strengthen and your knee can be stronger than it ever was before, so you can really get back to what you want to do or start new things that you have never done before. New experiences are what life's about. And your kids want to experience it with you!

If you don't take that time when they are babies, it's like building a house on quicksand—things fall apart. If you start lifting weights, running, and doing other things before your pelvic floor is ready, your pelvic floor and/or deep core is so weak that you can end up with a prolapse, leaking urine, or back pain later in life. You could end up with incontinence for the remainder of your life, and you don't want to do that.

Wearing pads and diapers to work out all the time doesn't need to be your way of life.

So, start resting, rehabilitating, and creating routines to restore your core now. It's never too late.

LOVE FITMAMA CHAPTER TAKEAWAY

1. Stay flat for five. Don't take the stairs for the first five days, or just use the stairs once per day, maximum.

2. See a pelvic health physiotherapist. Ask questions. Learn about your body, so you can reconnect, not disconnect.

3. Start a routine of focused breathing time every day. Five minutes is a great start.

CHAPTER 6

Rest Is Best

"Self-care is never a selfish act—it is simply good stewardship of the only gift I have, the gift I was put on earth to offer others."

—Parker J. Palmer

I will be the first to admit that I am a recovering, rushing, busy woman. When my babies were tiny, I used to let not one moment pass by that I wasn't doing something purposeful. I thought rest was for the weak and was a waste of time. Even after I hurt my back and needed to rest even more, I still resisted it, thinking I had no choice but to keep living my busy life as a mom.

Rest is a massive piece of the puzzle on the pregnancy and postpartum journey. In reality, the issue isn't that we can't rest because we have too many things to do or have to chase a toddler, it's that we don't even remember how it feels in our mind to be rested.

Really getting deeply into that place of rest is tough for us *warrior-type women,* who don't allow ourselves to enter that space, because as soon as we have a spare moment, it's on to the next thing! What else will we do? How can we cram more into this timeframe? And then, lest we forget how guilty we feel if we rest or ask for support for things we "technically" could do ourselves, we feel bad about ourselves or putting others out if we do rest. We feel lazy, we feel like we are not strong enough, or can't manage it all, or we feel we are neglecting our responsibilities. These are false evidence appearing real, or FEAR.

People hear me when I say rest, but the real question I get is, "HOW?"

Your true responsibility during this time of your life is you and your baby or other kids. Too often we put all our energy into the baby and don't keep any for ourselves. There is a way to get there without guilt. There is. You just have to want it and know how to get it. Feeling guilty about what you do or don't do and feeling guilty about what you eat or don't eat is a horrible way to live this period of your life.

Instead see this as a beautiful opportunity to watch your newborn grow into an infant, your infant grow into a toddler, and yourself grow into your role of mother. If that's all being clouded by rushing, impatience, and guilt, it's going to totally ruin the experience. Stop feeling guilty around food if you want to lose weight postpartum. Food is fuel. Food is nourishment. Food is pleasurable, and there is a way to make it so, even when you have weight-loss goals. It's time to change the conversation in your head that's telling you that you don't even have time. Time is an illusion.

Studies have shown there are no adaptive or motivational properties of guilt. Guilt only leads to a sense of loss of control, and the associated emotions of regret and shame that increase the stress response of the nervous system. This puts you in that constant elevated, high beta wave state of mind, which is in the "fight, flight, or fright" stress-response mode, feeling overwhelmed and out of control.

It keeps you in that state instead of letting you rest. You are stopping yourself from true rest if you are constantly going, doing, and burning the candle at both ends. It isn't about vegging out in front of the TV or spending all day on the couch, though it might look like that at times. Rest is about releasing control and only then can you deeply allow it to take place and nurture you.

To help clarify and lay out for you how rest starts to take place, I created this simple rest model to see for yourself how it comes together.

Rest

The three key things involved in taking rest are acceptance, asking for help, and allowing time.

Acceptance

Accepting is understanding that you need to rest, accepting that this new way of life is going to take away your sleep and a lot of your previous freedoms. It's going to take away certain activities you might have relied on to keep you feeling great, but it's also going to add so much more to your life overall. If you can, accept this new perspective, welcome it with open arms, and don't try to be a hero. Heroes know better than to hurt themselves just when they are needed in battle. Motherhood is a marathon, not a sprint. Your baby and your body deserve you to accept, right now, that you require rest.

Ask for Help

In addition to accepting that you DO need rest, it's a must to ask for help. Ask those around you. People constantly want to help, and we push them away. They are not just "trying to be nice"; they actually want to help. "Hey friend, can you watch the baby while I take a shower or a bath? Can you help me do this one thing? Can you help me while I go do this?" It's not selfish to ask for help. It's self-preserving, it's survival. Undoubtedly you know a friend that you would help when he/she needs you. Why would it be any different toward you?

Allow Time

Allow time and don't rush the rest. Rushing rest is not rest. Moreover, allow people to help you. As I said, people want to help. Asking isn't enough if you still "feel bad" or rush the whole time. ALLOW. Give yourself permission to accept help. And if you allow people to help you, you allow for the time that will be needed for you to recover from pregnancy and birth. Nobody can tell you how long that is, you must tune inward and find out for yourself. Trust that you can just allow for this space and time to happen for rest, without the guilt. Remember, it's a choice. You are not a victim.

When you can *accept, ask, and allow*, you can start to be more *relaxed*. You can start to be *realistic* about what you are capable of at this time. And you start to more deeply *receive*.

You start to receive help, support, strength, healing vibes, love, and understanding from those around you. Because they see you asking, accepting, and allowing for this time of rest to be a part of your life. They see you honoring yourself. And once you receive, relax, and are realistic with yourself, then you stay in this calm, peaceful place of restfulness. Doesn't that sound nice? It can be yours!

When we are not constantly in a rush, we gain perspective and realize that this time, while it feels like complete chaos, won't last forever and is a true gift. There is a saying, "The days feel long, but the years feel short." So true, right? The days can feel so long sometimes when we haven't slept or if we are all alone. If we could repeatedly tell ourselves daily that it's okay to rest, because the more stress and anxiety we feel in this postpartum window, the more stress and anxiety our children will feel and reflect to us. It starts to work counter to what we want in our lives. So, receive, be realistic, and just relax.

FITMAMA FOUNDATION: Rest is essential and not to be taken lightly.

Actively choosing to relax and being conscious of what it takes for you to relax are the places to start. Letting those muscles of your abdomen relax fully while you inhale, letting it all out, and opening yourself to the beautiful possibilities that rest and breathing deeply will bring. Create the relaxation response that your body wants to feel at the level of your nervous system.

Find Your Sisterhood

As humans evolve, things change. One of those changes is the village style of raising children—when there were smaller communities, less technology and distractions/busyness, full-time moms, and more. Now, so many of us are raising our kids in isolation and, besides a few playdates, we feel alone so many days and nights while we tend, teach, and raise our kids, often completely alone.

I have spent days and weeks on my own with my kids due to my husband's work travels. It's a choice we make, but it doesn't mean it's an easy one. Creating a community around me has been one of the most valuable assets. We are social creatures, and we need one another in this world, especially when times get tough.

Write a list of the top three things you need from your loved ones. Allow yourself to daydream, for example, if you think you could get a full night's sleep if so and so helped you out, write it down! Maybe your dream is to get that person, whose cooking you love, to make you a meal, so you don't have to worry about dinner for a night or two. Maybe you can ask that person, who has been wanting to know what he or she can do, to buy you a few meals from a healthy restaurant. Ask for what you need from your loved ones.

Create the village that women once had around them in the postpartum period. Isolating yourself postpartum is a fast track to postpartum depression (PPD), postpartum anxiety, or baby blues. We all need a community and support! Unless you are willing to ask and put yourself out there, you won't receive it. If you aren't sure what you need, and you don't know how to ask for it, you won't get it. Stop. Breathe. Make a plan.

Make Courageous Choices

As I have been saying, you have choices. We often act as victims of our circumstances, not admitting to ourselves that we have the choice to change things. When my business started picking up, and I was helping more and more people and connecting with others around the globe, I had a hard time setting boundaries. I got such a rush from connecting, helping, supporting, educating, and inspiring others that I didn't even realize that I wasn't taking the time to refill my own cup so I could keep going.

Going full tilt is NOT a long-term sustainable solution. Just because Australia was waking up, when we were going to sleep in North America, didn't mean I had to be working around the clock. I found myself rushing all the time, saying no to things I wanted to do, telling myself there was never enough time, and missing out on precious opportunities to connect with my family. We all do this to some extent in different ways. We let others infiltrate our precious time. The hard part is saying no.

Preserving your own resources is where this all starts. We tend to say yes to others, overschedule ourselves, and then do you know who suffers the most? Those closest to us, because we have no time or energy for them. The ones we love most. Set boundaries for yourself and don't book ANYTHING when you have a newborn or feel exhausted.

We get so excited when we get home from the hospital that we want everyone to stop by and see the baby. Maybe if you are on maternity leave, you feel like you have all this time and you want to fill it and go, go, go! I am warning you, do not just pick up where you left off, if you were going full tilt until you gave birth. No, no, no. I encourage you to rest. Set boundaries and say maybe to a visit from one person a week, or every two weeks. One family member a week. One couple to visit or whatever works best for you. It's not about them. It's about you and nobody can feel you bad without your permission.

Just set your boundaries, because the space between visits when you get time alone needs to be the priority for your solid recovery. Booking yourself back to back is not the way to rest, recover, and rehabilitate from having a baby.

So, set those boundaries, make some rules for the sake of you and your baby and the hardest part, but the most important, is to stick by them. This goes for right after birth and any time! Give yourself the time and space you need. Spend time alone with your baby, your partner, and yourself. Nurture those relationships with deep and consistent attention, reverence, and unconditional love. They deserve nothing less.

Delicate Discipline

Remember, no stairs for the first 5 days at least, or 7–10 days, after birth. Can you commit? If those days have already passed for you, then how about no running until you have fully rehabilitated? Running is not the be-all, end-all of weight-loss magic. Actually, it's not highly correlated with long-term weight loss at all. Even if, mentally, you can't wait to get back to it, your pelvic floor doesn't want you to run yet.

Running requires 8–12 weeks minimum of rehab (from when you start), and 8–12 months would be more ideal. Do not rush! Please take your time getting back to this exercise and all activities. Think of other things that you might be able to do for yourself that are more supported. Think cycling, ergometer (rowing machine), seated weight training, or other more pelvic-floor protected activities.

The less pressure you can put on your pelvic floor (you put pressure on your pelvic floor just by breathing) at first while you are retraining it, the better. Here is where the less-is-more approach is imperative. When it comes to high-impact exercise, avoid it for a bit, especially for the first six to nine *months* postpartum and if you are planning to have another baby.

It's important to take this time to rehabilitate and just breathe. Commit to no stairs at the beginning, and no running until you are fully rehabbed (talk to your pelvic PT for confirmation). I followed my no-stairs rule for my second baby, and I had almost two weeks less bleeding the second time around due to this. A significant difference to be sure, and that was just from taking the pressure off my pelvic floor and not running all over my house or going for walks too early.

So, I encourage you to really follow these guidelines. Remember giving birth is like a marathon—it requires training up to a point, and it requires a time period after for recovery and rehab. This is important. Don't skimp, or it will come back to affect your health in the future.

Guilt is a Crippling Emotion

Guilt, an emotion we are all familiar with feeling as moms, creates a stress response that will actually prevent our bodies from entering the "rest" mode of the parasympathetic nervous system. We all have choices to make each day—what to eat, what to do, where to go, how to spend our time or money, and countless other decisions.

Now, more than ever before in history, we have accessible to us at any one time more choices than we know what to do with. We are faced daily with the *paradox of choice*. "What will I eat today? What foods are best? Should I eat this, or should I eat that instead?" The media is always touting a different superfood or new fad diet that seems to be the be-all, end-all.

We probably had the guilt of shoulds and coulds before we had kids and now everyone is telling us what we should or shouldn't be doing with our kids. This feeling can truly paralyze us and trigger the making of poor choices. If we feel awful about ourselves and we're in a self-loathing type of headspace, how are our actions going to look coming from that place? If we feel like crap about ourselves and allow emotions like guilt to guide us, we then make choices that demonstrate how unworthy we feel. "Oh, look how out of shape/fat/lazy I've been, I might as well go to the drive-through; what difference will another fast-food meal make?"

We will always have myriad choices, and they will continue to increase, but the minute we come from that place of compassion and self-love, the choices change.

FITMAMA FOUNDATION: Feeling guilty is a personal choice you can choose not to make.

First, most often, guilt is a misplaced emotion. It stems from some other self-deprecating place, such as feeling low self-worth, low self-esteem, lack of confidence, or self-doubt. Feeling guilty is a choice. You can choose not to feel guilty.

I am going to give you at least one good reason why.

Feeling guilty will mess with our hormones. Feeling guilty stresses our systems and prevents our full potential for rest. It keeps us in "fight, flight, fright" mode and doesn't allow that "broaden and build" mindset to take over.

Start to change your perspective on what rest means. Start to see it as restorative, as rejuvenating, and as restful bliss that you deserve, need, and want. Please stop playing those same old records on repeat in your head, telling yourself that you are not worthy of the body and the life of your dreams, telling yourself you are lazy or need to do this or should do that or have to start Monday or whatever you are saying to yourself. Just end that. Please.

You have a choice.

LOVE FITMAMA CHAPTER TAKEAWAY

1. Accept that your body has undergone massive change within, and that your life has a "new normal" that takes some getting used to.

2. Ask for help. This obvious, but not-so-common, action makes a huge difference to how you feel and what you can handle.

3. Allow time. Now is the time your body needs to rest, relax, and recuperate. This time is paramount. There will be enough time.

CHAPTER 7

Rehab: No Pain, All Gain

"A setback is a setup for a comeback."

—T. D. Jakes

In my varsity basketball days at Queen's University, I was diehard into training to improve my game. I would lift weights daily, go in and shoot for extra hours, and I lived for pushing myself harder day by day.

This mentality has mostly stuck with me until now, but as I ease up and release this need to push myself constantly, I am seeing the benefits it is having on my life and my recovery from chronic pain.

Rehabilitating the core is a necessary part of having babies. Statistics estimate that almost 100 percent of pregnant and/or new moms have some level of abdominal muscle separation, called diastasis recti (DR), or core dysfunction present, which can lead to weakness, back pain, incontinence, prolapse, painful sex, pelvic pain, and other short- and long-term consequences of a weak and dysfunctional core.

Long-term symptoms of pelvic-floor and deep-core dysfunction are more common for those who had more than one child or had multiples (twins, triplets, etc.), demonstrating that the more intra-abdominal pressure (IAP), the more dysfunction can occur if prehab/rehab doesn't take place. Prehab is the work you do prior to giving birth to minimize the trauma, such as Pearl Pull-Ups™, core breathing, Epi-No™ pelvic floor trainer, proper Kegel pelvic floor exercises, and so on.

It's the IAP and core weakness from pregnancy that is responsible for the thinning of the linea alba creating the "separation" appearance of a DR. To "heal your seal," as I always say, take a long-term approach. Woman up, take personal responsibility for your body and core and their optimal function, both now and especially for later in life. It's not a time to get neglectful of self-care and it's not a time to push yourself through grueling CrossFit™ workouts at the expense of your future body, that is for sure. It isn't about giving up or throwing in the towel. It's about training smart.

Let's go back to the idea that I mentioned in Part 1 of this book about *embracing*: Imagine what you want to look and feel like 50 years from now. Beginning with that end in mind, take ownership about the fact that your body needs to do certain things *now* to function optimally *later*. We always think short-term when it comes to our younger years, and we don't think about what it will be like in 40–50 years from now. I know it seems so far off, but remember that "time flies" thing? It happens even faster as you go up in age I am told . . .

We want to move away from the "no pain, no gain" mentality of sport and move to the "no pain, all gain" mentality of the Love FitMama Way. By inflicting no pain on yourself as you rest and rehabilitate, you ease the pressure both on yourself in general and on your pelvic floor in particular.

Taking care of incontinence sooner rather than later is ideal. The more pressure you put on your pelvic floor before it's rehabbed, the greater the risk of dysfunction later in life; that could mean one or more prolapses and possible surgeries to correct it, whether it's bladder prolapse or another organ. Trust me when I say that you don't want this to be your story.

Rehabilitating and breathing loving life back into your private parts is really quite liberating and healing also. You grew a human in your core; it's time for nothing but reverence and pure relishing in and cherishing of your body. Knowing how to deeply connect with your core will help you function better in all areas of your body and your life. Pain, stress, anxiety, guilt, resentment, fear, and other emotions trigger physical pain in your body also, so in addition to your stronger deep core, your neck, back, legs, shoulders, and everywhere will benefit from this nurturing rest and rehab.

Sexually, you might find yourself to be more open to receiving orgasms (more and/or better) from your partner, and your deeper connection to your core will allow you to open up to self-stimulating orgasms (masturbation, if you aren't already).

Having one or multiple orgasms daily is one of the best things about being human, especially being a woman! This will improve your quality of life now and later on, which is what we are working on as FitMamas. Feeling good and living life now, with the love for our future bodies being a prominent motivator.

FITMAMA FOUNDATION: No pain, all gain.

I'm calling on your sense of personal responsibility to take care of your body and not worry about what everyone else is doing around you. Even if there are other new moms who are six weeks postpartum and they think they're ready for mom and baby boot camp—running, crunching, and jumping all around in the park—don't let that affect what you do. You might not feel ready to do that yet, and it might be months or years before you do, but don't let that deter you from taking care of your core from day one.

Others might not be tuned into their bodies (or haven't yet read this book), but you can choose to tune in to your body and listen to what your body needs. By listening to the pain, listening to the ways that your body is using to communicate, you can create this deeper core connection with yourself. Slowing down, quieting down, tuning in. What are the messages you get? Your body's wisdom and messages reflect that of your subconscious mind, so if something is paining you or causing issues for you, it's likely something that you're avoiding facing, such as burnout, exhaustion, cravings, anger, fear, or resentment. Even if it's a little headache, eye twitch or constantly getting sick.

For me, tuning out and continuing to push myself through workouts was how I operated in the past, but tuning in was the biggest life-changing experience for me. I couldn't NOT listen, when my injury put me in the hospital twice in a week when my youngest was one and a half. Before this, I was having severe back pain due to core weakness, and I didn't realize until much later that it was because I was completely in the "no pain, no gain" mentality.

If I wasn't in a pain-evoking/muscle-soreness creating/heavy-sweating workout, pushing my body hard, then I felt like it wasn't worth it. Like I wasn't working hard or something. I was doing this within six months of having a baby. For me, *as a trainer,* I told myself, I can handle it. I thought I was strong enough. I was superficially, but not deeply.

I needed to learn the lessons of patience, presence, and permission. But I surely wasn't doing what my body needed, nor was I learning it in this "no pain, no game" environment I set up for myself. So, in response, my body threw me a curveball that I just couldn't avoid.

The truth was that my hard-core, pushing-myself workouts couldn't have been further from what my body actually *needed* at that time. I was in complete denial, and I kept pushing. My body begged for rest and needed rehabilitation, and since it wasn't until after my injury that I *heeded my needs,* this pain went on to plague me for almost three years and it kept reminding me to stay the course when I veered off the LFM Way. From my experience of enduring the debilitating, chronic pain I have felt in my deep lower back, the *no pain, all gain* mentality was born. Now, if I feel pain, I stop. Go figure.

Retrain, Reframe, Regain

Even if you don't have pain right now, things might be happening on a subtle level deep in your body that you might not be aware of. It's time to start noticing the messages of your body, before they get too loud (and unavoidable, like mine).

First, as by now you know, it's absolutely imperative to *retrain your core.* What it takes to retrain your core starts with the simple act of the breathing exercises I teach, like the Pearl Pull-Ups™. You can access the LoveFitMama Private Facebook Group or the FitMama Global Facebook page and my website, www. lovefitmama.com. LoveFitMama group: https://www.facebook. com/groups/lovefitmama/ FitMama Global: https://www. facebook.com/JenOliverFitMama/ I share this with you so that you can start understanding how it's less, that's more, and it's the nonaggressive approach that actually works in this case.

The core works completely through the breath. Breathing deeply reconnects the mind and the body, as the mind and the body (specifically core-breathing patterns) can disconnect due to the many pressures you experience physically on your pelvic floor while you are growing a human inside your deep inner core. As I mentioned earlier, when pregnant and growing your little one(s), your body starts to change and your natural breathing rhythm naturally starts to change due to the IAP in the core.

If you aren't prehabbing or rehabbed, your muscles of the pelvic floor are unlikely to be able to withstand the pressure and can cause dysfunction, diastasis recti, back pain, and so on. The coordination of the muscles changes with the pressure, and this is where the retraining proves to be vital in connecting the neurons and brain-body pathways back together. This daily retraining using breathing is important to reduce risk of future core injury.

Belly Binding

I am often asked about belly binding. If it's done right, it is a great way to support the natural healing of your core. There are a few different types and styles, and my recommendation is that you get a belly binder from someone you trust. Don't just buy one online. Talk to a doula, your midwife, or a trusted trainer who understands the anatomy and physiology of the core. It's been shown to help with diastasis recti (DR), but it is only really valuable to do for the first 8–10 weeks postpartum. It might be comfortable to wear after that, but it's not necessarily going to add to your success.

Eight to ten weeks of time postpartum is the time that your body is naturally rehabbing, and after that, the binding hasn't been shown to be effective. I created a video for the LoveFitMama YouTube channel, which demonstrates how to do the belly wrap correctly. Doing it incorrectly can have consequences, such as creating intra-abdominal pressure (IAP) and pushing more of your organs down toward your pelvic floor, which will do more harm than good.

Something else that needs to take place during the course of your Love FitMama journey is critical thinking and perspective shifting. I call this "doing the undoing" or *reframing*. Starting to undo the way you used to look at things, and create new perspectives. When you start to reframe the way your workouts look in your mind, you will know that you can ease into exercise and still call it a workout. Know that an integral part of working out is rest and recovery.

One thing I did at least once a week, when my babies were little, was go to the gym and lie there stretching, or I would sit on a mat and not move, just enjoying the peace and not having to do anything for a brief time. That was my workout that day. It was just an opportunity to get out, to get space, to get into a different environment, and to allow someone to watch my babies for a couple of hours while my hubby was working, and I was wanting to take some time for myself.

You don't have to go and beat yourself up on equipment to have a good workout. I did listen to my body some days and I would just lie there and breathe, because that's what I needed. Working out is purely for you. It's YOU time. A workout can be anything you want. After I hurt my back, I craved my gym dates with myself, so I would go and just walk on the treadmill. Often, I'd listen to an audiobook or a podcast. Sometimes I'd listen to quiet music. I would just breathe and relax my nervous system, which is usually high in overdrive in new moms.

I didn't realize at the time how amped up I always was to go hard. Once I could no longer do that, my workouts looked different, but it was my headspace that was the most different. I completely saw things differently after my injury, mostly toward myself. There was no more of the pushing, and I was so much gentler and more nurturing. It took a while for this new mindset to become my norm, and it also took a little while for my body to get the memo . . . my body apparently has a hard time relaxing! But so does yours. Our nervous systems take longer than our thoughts to adapt, but it is worth it. So, reframe your workout mindset and reframe what it looks like to get your workouts in.

Last, when it comes to *regaining* strength, think baby steps. Give yourself that long timeframe, like one to two years, to take the pressure off and then regain strength slowly again. Don't push yourself. If you were lifting heavy when you were pregnant, go really low postpartum. And if you're anything like me, I know I was lifting heavy when pregnant. I was doing bent over rows, and I was lifting maybe 45-pound dumbbells at the time. I remember this clearly; I was petrified of dropping one on my toe. I was probably seven or eight months pregnant and I couldn't see my toes. But it was really important for me to realize that while I was strong before kids, birthing a baby really changes things deep in your core where all your strength lies.

Start from square one, start from lifting nothing and just breathe—absolutely nothing more. At first, just do core breathing and body weight movement, other than holding your baby. As the weeks go on, slowly listen for pain-free ways to regain strength in a *no pain, all gain,* self-loving type of way.

Get Guidance

When you are first learning about core rehab, I encourage you to do a focused core rehab workout, where you start core breathing as soon as possible (the day you give birth or while you're still pregnant) and do either Pilates rehab (Pilates breathing and deep core breathing are most alike and less like yoga breathing). I recommend Bellies Inc and the MuTu System if you just had a baby. The FitMama 28 Day FitBlitz™ Program is the best next step to transition back to your workouts and gain strength from within. All these can be done in the comfort of your own home. Following a simple, detailed and focused protocol will teach you the basics of reconnecting to your deep inner core and give you ample time to practice. You might need 12 weeks; you might need six months or six years. Everyone is different; take your time.

Realize that when you're 50, or 50 years from now, it won't matter if you took three or six years to really rehabilitate your core. You'll be caring more 50 years from now whether you're wetting your pants when you laugh or play with your grandkids or great grandkids, or whether you're being admitted to a retirement home because you have incontinence and nobody wants to change your diapers.

So be mindful of the fact that this time is not to be rushed. This is a nice, slow, rehabilitation time. It's where you get to work on a deeper, inner effort of you being a FitMama for life. This is what I'll be sharing more of in Part 3: Enjoy: Innercise before Exercise.

Hypopressives

Technically, all the mainstream ab exercises, such as sit-ups, crunches, planks, and Russian twists, are hyperpressive, meaning they increase downward pressure on the pelvic floor and increase IAP overall in the core. HYPOpressive exercises do the opposite. They lower the pressure in your abdomen and actually strengthen and tone the pelvic floor and deep inner core with an apnea-like breathing technique that has been shown to support the pelvic floor and promote proper core function.

Most of the activities that we do daily, like walking, bending, lifting, lying down, and sitting up all increase IAP, so this training method is highly recommended. Learning ways to strengthen your core and work to flatten your abs without conventional ab moves that create imbalances, dysfunction, and more downward pressure is vital, especially if you are already living with incontinence, prolapse, or another core dysfunction.

Just taking time for you in those first few months after birth to breathe, walk, create space, and move is all you need—nothing more, really. Once you can start to retrain, reframe, and regain, you start to cultivate that patience with regard to your workouts. You start to persist, because you don't burn out or hurt yourself. Then your workouts become more regular. And you start to pursue deeper core action, where things have more and more meaning to you because you've taken the time to slowly retrain and regain. You've come from that place that you know you're building a solid foundation for your "dream house" through your core.

FitMama's #StrengthenYourRoots philosophy is vitally important during this transition to motherhood when you're strengthening the roots of your body physically and retraining the core. And similarly, while you are focused on taking care of and nurturing your new baby and raising children, you are also strengthening your roots in your community, as a human being and a contributor to society and the greater good of all—raising the next generation.

This is a tall order, but I know you are up for strengthening your roots as a mom. Being present, really being there, with your children while you're feeding them, changing them, snuggling, and loving them is what the Love FitMama Way is all about. Knowing that you're just there in that moment exactly where you need to be, not worrying about your belly rolls or planning something else to do.

While you are reading, enjoying, connecting, and being, just know that you don't have to be somewhere else, you don't have to run off to a workout or clean or rush around, you can just relax. Take that pressure off yourself for the first few months at least and just rehab. You can just be living from that place of patience, in those present moments, pursuing things that are in the best interest for your baby and you. No pressure to clean or run errands. Take it off yourself, and don't allow anyone to put it back on.

What's most important to you at this time? In the middle of all the chaos that new babies bring, it's an opportunity for you to take a stand for yourself and what you believe in. The self-value generated from creating boundaries, breathing daily, and approaching yourself and your body with love, reverence, and compassion is big.

It creates that deeper integrity within, physical integrity in your core, yes, but also that deeper integrity for you as a human, when you slow down and start to look at things in a different way. This rehabilitation process and time period allows for that chance to look deeper into what's really going on and feel all the feelings, mentally, physically, and emotionally. Are you really heeding your needs, or are you stuck in a push-harder mentality that is working against your greater good?

LOVE FITMAMA CHAPTER TAKEAWAY

1. See a pelvic health physiotherapist; it is an absolute must. Regardless if you had a vaginal birth or a C-section, first thing when the six-week checkup comes, make an appointment with the physiotherapist for a full, deep-core assessment and pelvic exam. Share any pain or concerns you are having.

2. Belly binding, if done right, is a great way to support healing of your core.

3. Follow a plan. Remember, fail to plan, plan to falter. Follow a program or have someone guide you through the rehab process.

CHAPTER 8

Routine: Repeat and Rewire

"You'll never change your life until you change something you do daily. The secret of your success is found in your daily routine."

—John C. Maxwell

Now that we've got you into a flow of resting and rehabilitating your body and your mind, we're going to look at creating daily routines that help support your new habits and let you stay in your flow.

Are you someone who loves routine? Most people are, as routines help us feel safe, secure, and they keep things simple. You will learn how to prioritize, prep, and position yourself for the things you want to get done each day.

I can't count how often I hear people say, "I can't wait to get back to my routine," or "I got out of my routine and then I never got back into it." Routines are powerful forces in our lives, and they help us in so many ways. They can also hurt us, though, if we create routines and habits that don't serve us or aren't aligned with our greater good.

When we have babies, it seems we are always trying to get into a routine, and the lack of consistency in it can start to frustrate even the most patient of people.

I am talking here about creating routines that serve you through adopting and maintaining healthy habits.

Self-Sabotage

So many of us try to set ourselves up for success, yet we are unaware that we leave all kinds of opportunities for self-sabotage standing in our way. Self-sabotaging is any behavior that you engage in which stands in the way of you achieving the goals you set for yourself. Via the many forms of distractions available today, it's a wonder that we get anything accomplished! It is seemingly harder than ever with smartphones and screens in every waiting room, devices in every hand, and more things daily that require our attention. Procrastination, avoidance, and eating low-quality foods that take you further from your goals are all self-sabotage behaviors that will hold you back.

Are you aware of any of these that you are doing?

I want to help you set realistic priorities and minimize the potential roadblocks. This is why I created the FitMama Foundations™ online training program. It's specifically to help FitMamas cultivate healthy habits *that stick*.

to follow through, rather than go back to the old sabotage patterns. Don't make things harder than they need to be. Keep them simple, and create "if when-then" statements (I'll talk about these later in the book in Chapter 10).

FITMAMA FOUNDATION: Get comfortable living in the gray. Your world is never just black and white.

When it comes to creating routines that work for you, it needs to start with being realistic. So often we think of an ideal situation where we are able to run every morning, or go to the gym exactly when we want every day, or whatever the case might be, and these are completely unrealistic within the confines of your current life situation.

What is realistic for you right now to achieve? What is something small you could do, in addition to what you are already doing? Whenever we pair new habits alongside ones we are already consistently doing, the likelihood of sticking to them is much higher. You already brush your teeth every morning, so right after your dental hygiene, you could add something small, such as doing 10 Pearl Pull-Ups™.

Overhauling your life this is not, but it is attainable and realistic. You are already brushing your teeth. If you start to pair these two activities together, they will become part of your morning routine. A daily habit that helps you connect deeper to your core and you. What a great way to start the day! No matter what you want your new routines to be, it's imperative that you create a realistic set of expectations for yourself and start small. The journey of a thousand miles starts with a single step.

Another incredibly important piece relating to routines is who you surround yourself with. We all know those people who don't want to make any changes to their own habits and feel confronted and defensive when we make a change. Even if this change doesn't directly affect other people in any way, there might be people who want you to continue living in an unaware state, acting in misaligned ways.

By surrounding ourselves with like-minded people, we feel lifted, inspired, and supported rather than pressured and guilty for positive changes we make. Often, we are surrounded by others who want to sabotage our efforts, because they aren't putting efforts into their own lives and it stands out to them, and then they want to hold us personally responsible. We then get this vibe that by being our best selves, we are somehow doing something wrong around these people.

So, be around others who lift you up, who want you to shine your light, and who want you to respect yourself. Be discriminating in your life about what you do want and what you don't want to accept. If that person happens to be living in the same house with you, it can be even tougher. I have had countless clients whose husbands were completely uninterested in living a healthier lifestyle, and it was a great source of stress. I totally understand.

We cannot change others, though, only ourselves. Someone else holding you back is an excuse. We are the only ones who can stop ourselves from following through. Nobody, regardless of what they say to you, such as "Come on, that's so boring, let's order pizza," can actually put the pizza in your mouth, but

YOU. You choose. And it's not all about relying on willpower or self-control. I will go into what it really takes to do this in Part 3 of this book.

Last, one of the most incredible ways to stay in action mode toward your own goals is to support someone in his or her goals. The best way to learn something is to teach someone else, right? As humans, we want to be happy; we want to feel loved and supported. Why not be that person for someone else? Especially if this message resonates with you, and you are loving this idea of taking the pressure off yourself, starting to take more actions that honor your needs, then spread that message to others and help them embrace, nurture, and enjoy their motherhood journey along with you!

Studies show that having a workout partner or accountability buddy increases adherence to new habits significantly more than if you aren't following up with someone or meeting someone to follow through. Share the message you've learned with your friends and family—teach them about breathing, asking for help, core rehab, retraining postpartum, and the important message to rest.

These concepts help us elevate and allow us and others to not be pressured into doing activities that aren't safe for us, or to not be pressured into eating foods that don't nourish us, or to not speak to ourselves negatively because everyone else is self-deprecating. You can set a new standard for yourself and be the encouraging, shining light for others in your life who deep down want the same thing as you . . . to just feel good. We all just want to feel good.

FITMAMA FOUNDATION: It all starts with love.

When we share love and show love to ourselves, we give permission to others to do the same for themselves. It begins.

So, support others in their goals, be there for someone else because it not only allows you to teach others in a way that reinforces it for yourself, but it also allows you to support others in a way that reinforces your desire and positivity. It keeps your self-care at the top of your mind, when you are helping others with theirs.

We are all connected; we are all the same. You are me, I am you. We are connected. And the more openness we create within ourselves, the more openness we can share with one another.

Back Yourself

This is of absolute importance. You come first. You deserve unconditional love from you. Nurturing you and your needs is number one. As we start to discover what works best through awareness and reflection, we can begin to cultivate the new habits that serve our highest good. All that you are learning in this book is planting seeds in your mind.

When you water the seeds, nourish them with love and grow them through action. You create the beauty of what's possible for you. Together we are going to cultivate the habits that you want to create, so they no longer require willpower to make them happen. Willpower is not a long-term strategy.

Trigger Happy? Or Trigger Sad?

My husband is what I would call a minimalist, and there are few things he likes more than seeing clean, clear, and clutter-less spaces. I am less focused on this, and the result is often clutter developing on counters, tables, or in drawers. I can sometimes feel my husband get triggered by messiness when he walks into the house after work. He looks around and it adds to his levels of stress if things are out of order.

I am sure you can relate. Do you ever walk in the door and start to freak out inside, because things are messy and you already have a million things to do, and instead of facing those feelings and taking action, it triggers you into a negative cascade of feelings you'd rather avoid? It's triggers like these that lead you reach for a bag of chips, a glass of wine, or you resort to anger, bitterness, or resentment because you feel like you can't handle it all. This is an example of a trigger that can undermine even the most devoted of goal getters.

Awareness is vital. What are your personal triggers? Feeling overwhelmed, like you have no control? Too many things to do, and not enough time? Is it feeling alone, or feeling unappreciated? Is it feeling like you have no help or support? When we can observe our own behaviors and the mindsets that prompted them, we open our eyes to what's going on so we can appropriately make shifts and rewire our mind-body habits from what we see currently happening to what we want to see happening.

What is a 15-minute self-care routine that will help you unwind and that you would look forward to? What is it that you like to do? What will shift your headspace in this moment to see that a mess doesn't have to mean all is lost? It doesn't have to mean things are out of control. It could just be a reflection of a full day that needs a little wrapping up. What can you actually do in that moment of being triggered to alter your state? Do something that will remind your body how to feel good again repeatedly and retrain your brain so that this new perspective becomes part of your daily outlook. Making concepts mean something they really don't adds to your stress and keeps you stuck in a victim mentality.

I am here to open your eyes to the possibility that you do have enough time and you can get your self-care in, regardless of how many times you are triggered during the day by work, kids, in-laws, partners, or parents. Whoever or whatever it is, you can deal with it. It's not magic. It's grounded in science. It's so simple. It's not easy, but it's really quite simple to make the shifts.

The part that will make it easy is the repetition. Again and again. Breathe. Be kind to yourself. Repeat. It doesn't happen overnight, but neither did the habits you currently have form overnight. Together, we'll plant the seeds of what you want that future to look like. It might feel like it's far away or you're too far gone, but that's just your negative head talk, it is never too late to start. I'm currently working with an incredible 78-year-old client who desires a more peaceful mindset and more compassion toward herself. I am watching and experiencing core transformation within her before my eyes. It starts with appreciation, self-care, and gratitude.

Let Intuition Guide You

Everyone has an opinion. Sometimes we feel like people always want to tell us what to do, what to eat, how to do our jobs, or how to raise our kids. We can become filled with self-doubt, which really eats at the core of our being. Confusion, jealousy, uncertainty, and feeling stuck can be the result. Do you get those feelings often?

When you're sitting and look down and see your body, maybe the belly rolls that you have told yourself are bad for so long, it might seem impossible to love your body. You might feel unworthy of love from others, and it will make you act in ways that disrespect yourself. But your body has only love for you, and it just wants to protect you and support you. This negativity will keep you stuck. Looking down won't help you.

What you want to do is to start looking up and forward, to what is possible, what you want in this life, and how you can make it happen. When you look up, you are looking into the third eye. The third eye chakra is the seat of your intuition, the place you connect to truth, things unseen. While chakras are beyond the scope of this book, connecting deeper to your third eye will help you feel more centered, tuned into your instincts, and more self-aware of what your intuition might be communicating to you.

You can feel separate from others and even from yourself. But breathing and meditating, while focusing on the space just between your eyebrows, will give you a powerful connection to the universe around you and within you. Beginning with the end in mind, what do you want your body to look like and feel like when you are 50, 60, or 70? How about 100 or 110? Are you engaging in self-talk or behaviors that reflect how that body will look and feel in the future?

With current and future medical interventions, ideally we are likely to live to be old. So, begin to make peace with your body and befriend it. Create a daily routine that includes talking lovingly to your body until it becomes a way of life. Thanking your body for all it has done for you is a great place to start. Appreciation, compassion, and gratitude for yourself are the starting points for self-love.

Trees are intricate, and they live many years withstanding the elements. This is because they have strong and intricate root systems.

We are the same. We know it takes a village to raise children, yet we insist on taking it all upon ourselves. Start to strengthen your roots with the end in mind, with your children's children in mind. A tree is a metaphor for life and connection, to your kids and to yourself. And reconnection actually reveals itself through disconnection.

What I mean is that as we disconnect from our distractions, like old habits, social media addictions, TV, alcohol, or drugs, comparing ourselves to others, self-doubt, or whatever your choice of distraction is, we can start to build new connections to replace those. We can get lost in the addictive nature of distractions. They allow us to NOT feel for a while, when we really don't want to feel. When we get into these distractions repetitively, while avoiding what's actually inside us and dealing with it, the chemicals in our brains and our bodies are back in the fight-flight-or-fright response of our stress hormones. This contributes to acting like a trigger for more of the same behavior.

Stress hormones increase sugar cravings and other ways to make ourselves feel temporarily better. The above distractions act as triggers for the hormone release, just in the same way that alcohol or other drugs do with mind-altering chemicals. These chemicals rule our bodies. Stress and drama in life is the same; it produces this cascade of hormones that keeps you stuck in survival mode. There is no space for broadening and building in that mode. There is no space for self-care and self-love.

Without knowing, you might just be in an addictive chemical pattern with stress. You might not be consciously choosing it, but your cells have memory. When you learn something when you're young, it can imprint on your mind and body forever.

FITMAMA FOUNDATION: Disconnect to reconnect.

"Almost everything will work again if you unplug it for a few minutes, including you" (Anne Lamott). What you want to start to set up are these moments throughout your day where you can disconnect to reconnect to you and what's around you. When you disconnect during down times and spend more quality time with your present moment, rather than mind-numbingly scrolling through your Facebook feeds, you can start to break free.

The old, negative, hormone cascade will not get triggered, because you aren't watching others, comparing yourself, getting jealous, catastrophizing your own situation, and assuming everyone but you is having a great body and a great life (which is what social media most often portrays). This freedom is liberating. You do not need to achieve any of those things others have, just liberate yourself.

There is a theory called Hebb's Law (named for Donald O. Hebb, a pioneering neuropsychologist). Simply put, he proposed that "Neurons that fire together, wire together." What that means is that when brain cells activate at the same time, they connect to each other. I mentioned his name earlier in the book, but to explain further, Pavlov's work on classical conditioning was such that he was pairing signals together and seeing how they related to each other with repetition. He was training dogs to associate food with a ringing bell, to see if he could eventually evoke a salivation response just from the sound of the bell. He was successful, and his work became the foundation for understanding conditioned behavior. This is why I made the recommendation to add your 10 Pearl Pull-Ups™ routine to your teeth-brushing routine. You might think you don't have time, but, I assure you, you do.

Hebb's Law can demonstrate to you that you have fired and wired many connections that might not be serving you. Often, a habit starts out just once, and then it becomes more and more a part of your life. This means that you have probably conditioned yourself into certain behaviors triggered by the stress response of adrenaline pouring into your system. You might even be addicted to that without realizing it.

Those hormones are like drugs that our bodies can crave. Have you ever heard of being addicted to drama? This is the reason that it's even a thing—the stress hormones. The good news is that once you become aware that this is triggered by an old, undesirable habit pattern, you can start uncoupling those neurons so they don't fire together. This will stop triggering the stress reaction that keeps you stuck in a negative pattern.

So, for example, shutting down Facebook for a few hours (or days) means those neurons that register the usual response don't fire together. This gives your mind a little pause and lets you look in a different direction and maybe head down a new road, instead of the old, well-worn path. That new road is going to look a little bit different and, yes, might feel a bit scary.

What effect would this have on your behavior though? Maybe, instead of being stressed out and reaching for the chips or wine as usual, you might get to the cupboard or the fridge and decide you don't want them. You might decide to do something more constructive. You could go to another room and work on a project you've been neglecting, cut up some vegetables for dinner, do 10 minutes of tidying up, have a shower, or have a nap. Rewire those neurons to serve you instead of setting you further back.

Another aspect of this neural reprogramming project is the *observer effect*, meaning that *what you focus on, you see more of.* I already mentioned that your life is just a reflection of what you are putting out there. So, if you are finding your life is too busy, it's because you are putting out "too busy" energy and overcommitting yourself. If you are feeling unfit, or distressed about food and meal planning, that's because that's the energy you are sending out. This can come from comparing yourself to someone on line and downward spiraling into that old story that you don't have time or it's too expensive. What we need to do is break out of those feedback loops and attract better circumstances. Taking action cures this. Changing your self-talk is step one. Stop telling yourself why something won't work, and focus on how it will.

You might be saying, "I can't afford to eat healthier. I can't afford childcare. I can't afford a gym membership." This is a common excuse that falls in the false evidence appearing real (FEAR) category. Whether we grew up in a family where money was tight or one that spent money to alleviate boredom, guilt, or loneliness, we don't have to take those on as our own. If you are feeling that pinch of scarcity in your days, it's heavy, and you attract more of that. If you feel frumpy or bloated, you might be eating things that make you feel this way, but also just thinking about it is enough to attract it. Saying to yourself you are fat is going to keep you that way. If you want more confidence, you need to exude more confidence. Positivity begets more positivity. It's contagious.

What is it that you truly want to see more of in your life? I really want you to focus on recognizing this. So often we live by default and don't actively choose, we just let the old programs run. You get to choose, though, what you pair together, and that is a gift of being human. Your body is just your mind in action. What patterns stored in your brain are you repeating?

The answers to these questions start with nurturing your emotions, which takes us back to "Heed Your Needs" from Part 1 of this book. It's about asking yourself, "What do I need? What nurtures me? What am I not facing that I escape from by distraction? What is it that I am feeling that is keeping me stuck?" The self-awareness here is what you want to start building new pathways around. Check in with yourself often by breathing and being present, then the answers you are looking for will present themselves.

It starts with you asking yourself what exactly do YOU need to heal? What are these old emotional patterns? What has happened to you in the past that you haven't fully dealt with? You might think you have, but it well might be that you haven't. We all have bodies that are speaking to us to help us out. Where do you feel things in your body? I feel it in my back now, but before that it was always my belly. I would feel sick to my stomach if things weren't aligned for me. Now, knowing more, I can face that through love and understand the messages coming to me. Most often they are saying, "slow down, Jen; relax, Jen; be love, Jen; be present, Jen; all will get done, Jen."

How would you think and act differently when you come from a place of love? Some people talk about food journaling, as in writing down everything that they eat. This can be effective for some people, because it makes them pay attention to what they are eating and the patterns become easier to see. How would you feel and think differently if you created a conscious habit of paying attention to your feelings and looking for patterns triggered in your environment?

FITMAMA FOUNDATION: Look inward, and be the observer of your thoughts and behaviors.

An effective practice to start is thinking about rehearsing your days in advance. The research behind how visualization can positively impact outcomes is staggering, and I will share more of it in the chapters of Part 3. Essentially, though, your brain doesn't know the difference between real and imagined.

So, if you can practice rehearsing how you want things to go in advance of doing something, the prior rehearsing acts as if you have already been there and done that. If you practice daily, like athletes, musicians, or dancers, it can have the same effect in your everyday life. You can start to connect with your future self today by planning and practicing in your mind's eye (the third eye I mentioned earlier), the life you want to create for yourself. Then, daily take the actions necessary to achieve those results.

Get out your journal and write what you want your ideal day to look like. Write the details, what you want to spend your time doing, who you want to spend your time with, and how you want to feel with your kids or partner. Do this daily. Take the time. See it as if it is already done, and you will start to actually see things shift around you as you become that person. You are creating a map for yourself, identifying the ruts and dead ends you've been stuck in, finding the roads that will lead you to the top of the mountain, so you can see where you want to go and how you can get there.

Now that you've started mapping your journey, you can start planning the things you need to do to get there. What tasks do you need to do? What appointments do you have to keep with yourself? What delicate discipline do you need to employ to get you moving? What can you do to make meal planning quicker and easier? Make yourself a to-do list, put notes in your calendar, and put reminders in your phone.

Once you get into a groove of planning, you won't need to exert willpower to live the way you want to live. It will eventually become part of your daily rhythm of life.

At the same time, don't get discouraged if some days feel like you aren't moving forward at all. This is a lifelong journey. Everyone has low moments, so recognize them and shift, let yourself relax instead of judging. The road will still be there when you want to get back on it. No pressure.

LOVE FITMAMA CHAPTER TAKEAWAY

1. Choose small behavior changes you can achieve and pair these behaviors with self-care habits you are consistent with already.

2. Surround yourself with those who lift you up and support you.

3. Support others toward their goals to improve adherence to your own.

Part 3

Enjoy: Innercise before Exercise

Chapter 9

Love Is an Inside Job

"What lies behind us and what lies ahead of us are tiny matters compared to what lies within us."

—Henry Stanley Haskins

I don't know about you, but recently I realized that I've been trying to change my body for about as long as I can remember.

When I was 16, I remember doing crunches every day and calf raises on the step in my bathroom, because I read that stronger abs and calves would help me jump higher. And I desired to jump higher to play sports better. That was 20 years ago. It went on since then.

That's a lot of self-improvement and forcing growth. It isn't that I was dissatisfied though the whole time along the journey. And whether your goals are to gain muscle or weight, get faster, or lose weight, enjoying the journey is what the Love FitMama Way is all about.

So often we go through the motions. We eat foods and meals that we don't enjoy, but it's "on the plan" or "healthy." And we know we can eat what we want or binge another time after we are done with the plan or have fallen off the wagon.

The diet, fitness, and weight-loss industry breeds this. The gyms bank on it.

I encourage you going forward to begin all plans with the intention of continuing them for a lifetime. Yes, that can seem daunting at first, but it is necessary for true, lasting change. When you approach this scary-sounding task with the Love FitMama perspective, it will seem a lot easier. It's just one day at a time, one choice at a time.

Self-awareness is the goal, and that is different from the goal of perfection. If you can commit to yourself that you will find something you like to do for movement, and do it as often as possible (at least three to five times per week), then you will be taking loving care of your body, which you want to use and preserve the function of for as long as possible. You will start to tune in to your body instead of tuning out, and you will feel so good you won't want to not follow through. Self-love includes daily movement, which is what our bodies were made for. Cars were barely invented 100 years ago, and modern humans have been around for hundreds of thousands of years. It's incredible when you think about it.

The innercise before exercise that needs to get done is stepping back and taking stock of all that is going on around you. Ask yourself what you really want and need, and then cultivate a life filled with more of what you want and less of what you don't.

Simon Sinek, a world-renowned leadership consultant, talks about starting everything you do by asking, "Why?" Ask yourself why you want what you want. Keep digging deeper by repeatedly asking yourself, "for what reason?" to the answers you come up with. Because this will keep you going when times get tough. By being really clear with yourself about *what* you want and *why* you want it, you can start to weave that into the fabric of your life. Eventually, it will seamlessly transition as your new normal.

The three areas to focus on, with respect to enjoying your life and pursuing your *innercise*, are intentions, expectations, and obligations.

As I outline each of these in detail in the chapters to come, you can see in the enjoy model where intentions and obligations intersect. You have intentions to exercise and you haven't overbooked yourself, you follow through on your goals and you don't let yourself get sucked into putting yourself last. That's self-care.

When you minimize your obligations and maximize your expectations, you get a fierce sense of self-respect, which is more powerful than any sexy outfit, rock-hard abs, makeup, and a new hair style. Self-respect oozes off confident women who expect a high standard for themselves and say no to things that don't serve them, whether it's people or another trip to the drive-through. No judgment on yourself when you self-assess, just honesty with whether you really want it, or are you wanting it out of habit or old belief systems that have no place in your head?

When you maintain your positive intentions and you maximize your expectations of what's possible for you, you increase your self-love quotient (SLQ) as Eloise King, from The Self-Love Project, calls it.

The combination creates that beautiful fluid place called *flow*, where time and space are on your side, and you feel like you are truly where you are meant to be—enjoying life and everything in it moment to moment. Yes, this place exists and it is within you. Read on to reveal the steps.

Starting to get back into your old routines before baby is like trying to put on your skinny jeans the day you give birth. There is no point, things have changed and, for now, that's just not going to work. Why set yourself up for that? The same thing goes for the things you loved to do before kids, which are now unreasonable or impossible to expect of yourself. Let that go for now.

Before you can start on a new gym or boot-camp routine to build up the outside of your house (superficial, what people see) with exercise or a more organized, targeted meal plan, it's a must to get grounded and clear on your why. Why do you want to wake up early to go to the gym, why do you want to take one hour weekly to plan out your workouts, and is it a deep enough why to get you out of bed early in the morning or stay motivated long term? Dig deeper, if it isn't.

Without a clear why, you look outside yourself for answers. You don't establish yourself at the core of your desires and, therefore, you look outward rather than tuning in. It's as if others' opinions of us matter more than our own opinions within ourselves.

Turn that around. You are valuable and entitled (in the description that Elizabeth Gilbert gives for entitlement in her book, *Big Magic: Creative Living beyond Fear*) to your creativity, opinion, and uniqueness to share with this world. Remember, you are a FitMama now; this is about transforming the core of you, from the inside out, while loving yourself along the way. You have all the answers within you: which foods to eat to feel your best, which exercises to do that are best for you at this point, and there is no need to look outside yourself anymore.

Choose a program because it has some new routines or moves or is results-oriented toward what you want, but not because you think it's going to fix you, save you, or someone told you to do it. Start tuning out the noise around what others say to do, and start tuning in to what you want and have already in your life. This is how you enjoy your life day to day, now and in the future.

To cultivate a deeper innercise practice before focusing on your exercise practice, I recommend starting with making a commitment to yourself.

Commitment

Commit to making a change, no matter how big or small. We all know doing the same thing repeatedly and expecting a different result is pure insanity. *FitMama's 21 Days to Love Your Body* ebook and audios are available on the website, lovefitmama.com. Commit to focusing on how you can improve your inner wisdom and get closer to yourself through gratitude, mindfulness, and self-care. This program is all about tuning inward and starting to look closer at what is holding you back. You will cultivate more self-loving routines that reflect what you want at your core, not what someone said that you are supposed to eat or do.

Consistency

We all know consistency is key, but we still start and stop so many times. Set up a schedule and seek support, so you can stay consistent and not be yo-yoing all over the place. Sometimes putting yourself first, then ignoring your needs for months at a time, doesn't set a good example for those in your life to treat you with the respect you deserve. And you start to undermine yourself when you commit, and then go back on your word.

This drives a wedge into your own self-respect. Just create a realistic routine and stick with it, delicately disciplining yourself to repeat through all the roadblocks that life throws at you. Your self-care routines will serve to ground you and will protect you from the deep effects of the inevitable and constant ups and downs of life.

Courage

It takes a great amount of courage to honor yourself. Put on your big-girl panties and shout, "I'm worth it!" Keep going back to your new way, even when you feel you've failed. Fear of failure is an excuse you're making up to keep you stuck, and you're not accessing your personal resources of courage to break free. Who are you comparing yourself to? Have the courage to compare only to yourself, and ask yourself to step up and do your best in each moment.

Choose self-care, live from a place of gratitude for what you have, and keep expecting the best for yourself. Take personal responsibility of your life and let go of victimhood. Decide that if you want it, you have to be the one to make it happen. So, ask for help, do the hard work of trusting in the process, and tune in to your intuition for guidance. Nobody knows better than you. Be brave and go with your gut.

The concept of innercise is all about looking within and asking questions, such as, "Okay, is this thought or behavior supporting ME? My inner self? Those closest to me?" We are always so focused on the external self and the superficial way of what other people think, such as, Oh, my hair's bad. Look at hers, she must think mine is horrible." or "I have to wear the right clothes or else I can't go to the gym. People will laugh at me or see that I don't know what I am doing."

The Love FitMama Way is about you, NOT about anyone else. It's about getting more deeply connected within and allowing yourself the space to sense, feel, and listen to your inner voice, tune in to your breath, which is your loving, life-giving companion everywhere you go. Feel the sensations within your body that are trying to communicate with you. Allow yourself the time and the presence to really embody your body and feel how it feels to be you.

"Be more present" is such a simple notion that as a way of being it's become idyllic and not grounded in reality for most of us. We spend so much time in our heads! Western humans have created a culture that is busier and more distracted than ever, and we now look for "quick fixes," rather than good old-fashioned, slowing down and quiet time. Being present seems almost boring and, while we want it, we make ourselves believe that it cannot be what we are truly seeking, or it cannot fit into our life right now until something else happens first.

When we spend all our time in our heads, and we cannot stop worrying or stressing about the past or the future, we feel anxiety, regret, depression, guilt, shame, and unfulfillment. This low level of energy vibration we create with these emotions puts us into a place of expecting less. Low expectations of ourselves and others is counter to the Love FitMama Way. When we are anxious about things that might or might not happen, or we wish we could change things in the past, we cannot truly enjoy the moments that make up our life.

As Eckhart Tolle, the spiritual teacher, says in *The Power of Now: A Guide to Spiritual Enlightenment*, "Nothing ever happened in the past; it happened in the Now. Nothing will ever happen in the future; it will happen in the Now."

Are you taking personal responsibility for this exciting role as mom that you took on? Are you stepping up to your leadership role and letting go of old stories and excuses and doing the best for your family and you now?

Have you noticed yourself stepping up, or are you just going through the motions? It is a daily choice to do the inner work of listening to your own needs, taking care of yourself, and asking for what you need.

So, you can handle it like the leader I know you are, there are three aspects of enjoying your motherhood journey that I am going to specifically tackle in the last part of this book: *intentions, expectations, and obligations*. Mastering these for yourself will lead to better self-care and increased levels of self-respect and self-love.

LOVE FITMAMA CHAPTER TAKEAWAY

1. Self-care comes from maximizing your expectations and maintaining your intentions.

2. Self-respect comes from maximizing your expectations and managing your obligations

3. Self-love comes from maintaining your intentions and managing your obligations

CHAPTER 10

Set Intentions: Maintain the Magic

"Our intention creates our reality."

—Wayne Dyer

Setting an intention to get something done and then actually following through on it has almost become another mom joke, "I had the best intentions, but . . . *the baby was up, the kids were out of control, I was tired . . .* " and so on. These might sound like excuses, but, in fact, they aren't. They are merely *tests and pests.* Tests to see how much you actually WANT the desired outcome. These tests not only show you the answer (you didn't really want to get up and run, did you?!) but they also serve as pests that can wear on us and erode self-respect, self-trust, and our self-beliefs. They deplete us and they hang over our heads making us feel guilty (gasp! not another source of guilt)!

FITMAMA FOUNDATION: Setting clear intentions = magic.

To avoid feeling pestered by these little tests we carry out every day, we can start to create clearer intentions of WHY we want to do things, and WHAT, WHEN, and HOW.

Speaker and author, Simon Sinek talks about the concept of "why" in his TED talk and in his book, *Start with Why: How Great Leaders Inspire Everyone to Take Action*. The reason it's best to start with "why" is because it taps into the purpose, belief, or cause that inspires you. It's alive and real.

When you think about losing weight, putting in time and energy to your fitness, meal prep, self-care, meditation, journaling, or any number of other related goals, it can feel so hard sometimes. So. So. Hard. Especially on top of all the other things you are responsible for.

Another thing on the to-do list? *No, thanks.*

FITMAMA FOUNDATION: Anchor your intentions with your why.

Why do you want to lose weight? Why take better care of your body? Why go to sleep earlier? Why have more unscheduled days to rest? Why are your goals, dreams, desires, and intentions important for you to reach? WHY?

Once you start to tap into this why factor, you will start to create more meaningful intentions about those behaviors that contribute to your goals and, in turn, you will be more likely to carry them out. For example, looking cute, fitting into your skinny jeans, or looking better than your neighbor who just had a baby might seem like motivating intentions on the surface level, but these are NOT meaningful whys for most people. They will NOT get you out of bed when you're tired, they won't inspire you when you're depleted, and they won't increase your likelihood of success. These desires in and of themselves will not meet the standards of motivating you to take action.

Intentions, as I refer to them here, are about "maintaining the magic," and when I talk about the magic, I talk about the whimsical, can-do energy when you finally believe in yourself and repeatedly take action. It includes the intentions you have going into a new program or school year or anytime you have this "I will reach my goal" energy. Once you get the momentum from repeating new behaviors, you get the motivation to move forward.

Action precedes motivation. To maintain the magic, we have to set ourselves up for success without relying on willpower. Habits help us make healthy behaviors feel easy. "Habits eat intentions for breakfast" was a meme I saw and thought was so funny and true. You can set the best intentions, but habit formation helps us "maintain the magic."

Habits are what I help FitMamas create, and for moms living full lives, we don't have time to think about each choice throughout the day.

One of my favorite writers, Gretchen Rubin, talks about the four tendencies, or personality types, toward behavior modification and healthy habit creation. In her book, *Better Than Before: What I Learned about Making and Breaking Habits—to Sleep More, Quit Sugar, Procrastinate Less, and Generally Build a Happier Life,* she examines how personality and natural tendencies influence our success rate in adopting new behaviors. There are rebels, obligers, questioners, and upholders. I can tell what someone is with just a few questions, but I highly recommend finding out for yourself, at the online quiz at http://bit.ly/GRQuiz4Tendencies.

Rubin also has a great journal, *Better Than Before: A Day-by-Day Journal,* that comes with the FitMama Foundations™ program, and I highly recommend it. You can buy it online or at your local bookstore.

When people told me that my sex life would become nonexistent, or I would never be able to do the things I loved because I had kids, I didn't believe them. I stayed curious as to how I could be present and really live openly moment to moment to see how my story unfolded. This worked for me repeatedly in all situations. I am a rebel.

This helped maintain the magic for me of what was possible. How could I defy the odds? I like defying odds and knowing that I can choose the lens through which I see the world.

It's so easy to live in fear and not question what others have planned for us. People will hijack our time and as the modern proverb says, "If you don't stand for something, you'll fall for anything." Stand for you. Stand for being positive to your body and treating it with love and respect as any being on this planet deserves. Don't put others on a pedestal and knock yourself down and expect yourself to thrive. And don't knock yourself even lower.

You see where this is going, right? There's got to be something deeper to get you to stay on the path. One day the skinny jeans just won't be enough.

When you come down to the WHY, such as your kids, future self, partner, family, friends, community, and PURPOSE in this world, you will naturally be more motivated toward your goals.

Setting that clear intention of what it is going to look like is still the easy part, but it can feel hard to daydream or imagine what the future really looks like. Author Daniel Gilbert, in his book *Stumbling on Happiness*, shares the research that we really cannot imagine our future selves. That is why we have such a hard time delaying gratification or giving up things (especially vices or bad habits) in the now for future payoff of better health or no disease. It's too far off often to feel like a realistic threat.

FitMama breaks down setting intentions for self-care goals to three key areas for success: optimism, outlet, and owning it. It begins with optimism: Positive psychology is where I go to nerd out on the science and research of living a thriving, flourishing, Love FitMama life.

Psychologists Martin Seligman and Sonja Lyubomirsky are well-known researchers in the area of positive psychology and happiness, and they have found that having an optimistic outlook and seeing the "bright side" of things, even when they aren't great, can serve as a contributor to happiness. It's not about living in denial or avoiding reality, but more about creating the positive environment in your mind to "broaden and build" (a phrase coined by social psychologist Barbara Fredrickson), rather than coming from a narrow, survival-like mindset that comes from pessimistic, fear-based thinking.

Optimism contributes to seeing and creating opportunities, and it's closely linked in the literature with increased resilience, thriving, and flourishing, which are all key features of the Love FitMama Way. In his book, *Learned Optimism: How to Change Your Mind and Your Life*, Martin Seligman outlines the what, how, and why about learning to use optimism to improve your life.

Seligman explains that optimistic people approach life by believing that negative circumstances are manageable and they have a high sense of personal confidence that they can overcome any negative events. Optimism is related to many positive mind and body health outcomes such as lower likelihood of drug or alcohol dependency (and thankfully lower use of these substances during pregnancy), greater immune system function, prevention of chronic disease and living a longer life. Sounds worth it, right?

The second piece to consider when creating intentions is that you frame it as an outlet. When creating intentions about self-care, self-love, self-awareness, and self-trust, it can seem so boring, too much pressure and so much like you're just adding more items to your to-do list. We all know we don't have a lack for things to do as moms. So rather than tell yourself what you "need to, have to, should, could, or must do," I encourage you to start asking yourself questions, such as, "What do I love to do for me? What fills my cup and energizes me? What can I do more of that will make me feel better about myself?" Ponder these and write answers in your journal.

When we can start to have more self-awareness about the things we do or don't enjoy, it informs our actions, if we give ourselves permission. So often, we do things that we have been told we like to do, or we should like to do. But ask yourself what you enjoy. Maybe it's dancing or painting or walking or singing. Maybe it's something you haven't ever tried before. What have you not yet even discovered about yourself? I give you the green light to explore.

Last, when setting intentions, think about setting new standards for yourself and owning them! Own it, FitMama! Everything you do! Why not? Why let others make you feel like you're doing the wrong thing? If something works for your friend, it doesn't mean you have to try it or that it will work for you, especially if you feel stressed and overwhelmed.

Start to tune in to what your body wants. And if the newest fad diet or super food isn't your cup of tea, own it. If you want to do yoga, own it. Weight lifting? Own it. Hate the gym? Own it. If you want to do anything that makes you feel good, own it! Ask for the support you need to make it happen by changing your inner dialogue from "It's too hard" or "I can't" to "I can do it" and "How CAN I?"

As we start to see our self-care goals as loving, nurturing self-hugs, we can give and receive any time. All day, it is available for you to breathe deeply, sigh, walk, meditate, draw, color, sing, practice HeartMath®, snuggle or do countless other things that calm you, bring you joy, and allow you to reconnect with your truth, not your ego. Set for yourself an intention to live a more intentional, mindful, and aware life where you see, feel, and embody the value of taking care of yourself and how what you do, how you think, and how you act affects those closest to you and all around you.

It starts with a level of optimism and owning your story and your current situation. If you feel like you are over your ideal weight, be mindful that this body is here to teach you compassion, self-love, and patience, so accept the challenge and face it head-on. Or the lesson might rear its ugly head in another form of dis-ease in the future.

When you are optimistic and you own your story, you maintain the motivation to push, with vitality and passion, toward the goals you've set. If you have an optimistic perspective and you have a personal outlet, you will move forward toward your goals. And when you own your current body and situation and you have that outlet for you to quiet down and tune inward, you will mellow out. And this will feel, oh, so good.

Right there in the center is the sweet spot, where the magic happens.

Setting an intention for something you want is one thing, but maintaining your intentions when things get tough is the harder part. When things get difficult, we tend to put ourselves last, not justifying our own self-care. Self-love begins with self-trust.

Intentions

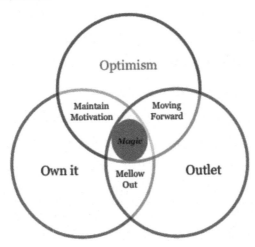

Trust

Trust the journey you're on and do less self-doubting and worrying about what others will think or if things are right or wrong. This one is a tough one. We don't want to hurt others' feelings, so we go along with things we don't really want. We follow paths, we don't intend to go on. One of my greatest teachers of self trust has been my own back injury and it still serves me to this day by pinging me with sharp pains or tightening up and gripping me to stop, slow down and survey what's going on within me and around me. We so often live our lives in fast forward, focusing so externally that we have no idea what's happening in our inner landscape. It's what's inside that counts, remember?

This is your wakeup call FitMama. If you are reading these worlds, it's time to take care of your needs. Assess your values and see if you are living in alignment with them. You are the only one who has to live with you inside, you don't want to be living for someone else. We have a joke in our family that states, "Nobody cares," and we say it in a tongue-in-cheek way with my parents and siblings, like, "Why do we worry so much what others think?"

Most people are so self-absorbed that they don't even notice what we are or aren't doing, being, having, wearing, or saying in any given situation. We ruminate about things that others don't give a second thought to. Just stop. Trust your deep inner sense of wisdom. This is your life's journey, not someone else's. Spend your energy more wisely.

Track

Get clear on what actions need to be taken on a daily, weekly, and monthly basis. What you track gets measured, and what you measure, you can see improvements on, which will motivate you. I'm not talking about having to track everything you do, but you can check off daily even one to five small items you have as non-negotiables. These will become as regular and routine as brushing your teeth. We never hem and haw about brushing our teeth the way we do about exercise. "I brushed them yesterday, and I'm exhausted. I don't have time, I will probably do it again next week," said no one ever.

Sometimes it can feel stifling to track what you do, and if it does, then stop. I had to get rid of my Fitbit tracker, because I found it creating an urgency within me that would register as pain in my back. I still move a lot and walk regularly, but

I didn't need the tracking to nudge me anymore. But do still hold yourself accountable. I'm excited at the prospect of using an activity tracker again, but I've accepted that now is not that time for me. I have a calendar in my meditation room where I put a heart on the date every time I sit for my daily meditation, journaling or stretching and breathing sessions. Track anything you want, especially if you are a details and numbers person who gets inspired by seeing things visually change over time.

Tribe

"Find your tribe. Love them hard." This was one of those quote memes going around online, and I think the origin was a gorgeous Danielle LaPorte #TruthBomb. Her messages are life-affirming. This is a concept of being surrounded by like-minded people who lift you, elevate you, and support you to become the greatest version of yourself, while they also call you out on your bullshit when you are selling yourself short.

You created a tribe by having a family, and you get to support and love them to be the best version of themselves. Not what you want them to be, but what they are meant to be. Find your tribe of like-minded people outside your home too. Whether online or in person, get connected with people who resonate with you. We have our https://www.facebook.com/groups/lovefitmama/, and if this book resonates with you, I think you will find your tribe there. Search for people who share the same values and speak about the topics you want to be speaking. Nix negative people who are dragging you down and keeping you stuck and feeling bad about yourself.

You deserve better than lowering your intentions to the norms of society. People around us are doing and saying crazy things, and we don't have to buy in. There is a new body positivity movement online, #bopo, and I am loving it. Women of all shapes and sizes have decided to stop shaming others (women and men) for what their bodies look like. What size we are or our body mass index (BMI) is a complex concoction of hormones, genes, lifestyle, and more.

We've created a culture where more than 90 percent of women are dissatisfied with their bodies and are attempting to change them in some way. The leader of the Diet Rebellion, naturopathic doctor Kerri Fullerton, delves deeply into the way the diet culture has primed us for this and how to stop buying in. Her wisdom is incredibly important information for us to understand, so we can create our implementation intentions in such a way that they lead us to the results we want, both short and long term. Being body positive, she explains, isn't about eating whatever we want when we want and becoming unhealthy and careless with ourselves. It is about treating your body with appreciation, love and respect and listening to it's guidance in what to eat. Health is a very real focus at The Diet Rebellion and they focus on rebelling against the diet culture that promotes restriction, shame, guilt and ultimately a rebound effect of binge eating, self loathing and/or weight gain.

Remember that energy you felt when you had a big project you were working on, and you were so engaged in doing it. Maintaining the magic is about maintaining that flow state in your mind. The flow where you are aligned. You set your intention, feel aligned in your beliefs, and take action toward that direction.

Remember how pumped and excited you felt when starting something new for you? Where you are like, "Okay, I'm taking care of me. I'm going to get better. I'm going to do what I need to do to meet my goals." You have these moments where you decide you are motivated and you are going to move forward. How long does that excitement usually last? We know from the data on New Year's resolutions that it's usually less than a month.

The truth is that to maintain the magic and that high energy feeling of setting an intention, we have to create the habits that reinforce that intention. And we keep coming back to compassion and love for ourselves. It isn't going to look perfect. Don't look for the perfect time or circumstance.

Creating daily habits are where the consistency and laying down of new neural networks come in. Ask yourself, what your intention was for reading this book. Why are you reading it? What is your intention with increasing your positive, healthy habits? Why do you want to cultivate them? Get back to that place when you first had the idea and then moved forward and took action. Ask yourself, "Okay, what habits need to actually occur in my day so that these intentions can be followed through." Because if we have great intentions in saying, "Oh! I'm going to this and that (and that)," and then we don't actually create those habits or follow through on those intentions then they really just flop, right? They actually never even get off the ground.

FITMAMA FOUNDATION:
Habits reinforce intentions.

In health psychology and behavior change research, there is significant support for implementation intentions as the way to build those habits based on their success in goal attainment. Implementation intentions are mapping out "if when-then" statements. So, for example, you are setting an intention to eat healthier. Creating habits about eating healthier comes from setting up your "if when-then" statements, such as, "If when I am needing to be up in the night with the baby, then I will switch my morning workout to lunch hour." "If when there are donuts served at the meeting, then I will say, 'no, thank you.'" Creating these statements allows us to have a plan to carry out our goals and allows us to create backup plans that are highly effective in ensuring you get the job done. Then, in the moment, decision making is not needed and preserves energy for other things.

Adding in this detail on the how, when, what, and who is helpful because research has shown that there is a gap between intentions and behavior, and implementation intentions can bridge that gap. When going further, you can start to problem solve in advance, "If the baby wakes up in the night too often, and I'm too tired to get out of bed in the morning, then I will pack my gear the night before, so it's ready just in case."

Research shows that we generally only have a few habit patterns in our days that are repeated on a daily and weekly basis. If you wrote down what you do in sequence from the time you get up until you go to bed, you will see that you follow the same similar patterns day after day. Weekends might be different, or if you have young children, it can be more random, but on average, we have routine lives.

You probably have a set routine of different habits that you've been doing forever. Once you start to create awareness of them (map them out, if it helps you get clarity), then you can see the areas where things aren't working for you.

FITMAMA FOUNDATION: Awareness of what isn't working for you is a key first step.

Have the courage to shine a bright flashlight on your habits and be honest with yourself about where you are acting out of alignment with your intentions and your values. Start to value and appreciate your body through cultivating a gratitude practice. It's easy to be hard on yourself, but that's actually NOT what's needed to move forward.

Noticing what, who, and why you are grateful is a key component to your Love FitMama life. Remember to keep closely connected to your positive emotional headspace and keep the things that make you feel good close. Use these tools to overcome the depletion of your self-control and maintain the magic that will transform your being.

You are the master of your own destiny, the leader of your life. Maintain your intentions for what you want, or switch them up for new ones that feel better. The magic is making your life and goals work for you. Don't constantly strive for ideals that others place on you without question. Own that you aren't a victim of your circumstances and take responsibility of your life and your choices.

The old blame, shame, stories, and scripts you repeat aren't getting you where you want to go. Create new ones through the perspective of optimism and aim high. Have an outlet: A space or time that you love to go to, and start working inward to heal the parts of you that are standing in your way. There is nothing to do but approach others and yourself with forgiveness and love, one day at a time. Start with yourself.

LOVE FITMAMA CHAPTER TAKEAWAY

1. Trust—in yourself in and your inner guidance. Developing a journaling and meditation practice support this trusting connection.

2. Track—what you want to improve on. Get clear, and set implementation intentions to set you up for success.

3. Tribe—surround yourself with supportive and like-minded people. You are influenced by those around you.

CHAPTER 11

Maximize Expectations: If Anyone Can Do It, You Can

"Our environment, the world in which we live and work, is a mirror of our attitudes and expectations."

—Earl Nightingale

People talk so much about how many things "change" when you have a baby, and it doesn't always sound positive. Sure, there are things that make parenting tough, but I like to think of becoming a mom as an opportunity for transformation. You might or might not realize it, but you are, in fact, experiencing the transformation right now.

You are transforming the former, single person you into the new you: MOM. It's an ever-evolving role. You're still you. You are now responsible for raising another human (or more). Being a FitMama is all about starting with love for you and about transforming the way in which you interact with the world around you. Transforming how you see the world and how you see yourself in it. This comes from growth and wisdom put into practice. Growth that comes from making mistakes and screwing up, but still trusting by learning from it. And with more practice, it creates more growth and wisdom.

Coming back to the creation of the new habits, routines, and new ways of thinking that I discussed in the last chapter, this transformation to motherhood is about creating new ways of being you in this world. As one of my mentors says, "Being more OF you, not more THAN you." This world, your kids, partner, coworkers, friends, family, etc., just want you to be you.

Setting high intentions and then maximizing the expectations of yourself and meeting them will greatly contribute to your self-confidence. Set realistic goals and intentions that are aligned with your values. Then crush them by following through. You can make it look effortless while you're at it. Wait, it CAN BE effortless while you're at it.

FITMAMA FOUNDATION: Be open, curious, and expect amazing things to happen in everyday life.

When it comes to how we see ourselves or others in this world, so much of it comes from the expectations we hold of how things are going to be. The world around us is a mirror as Earl Nightingale put it so eloquently in the chapter opening quote, our environment is just mirroring back to us our attitudes and expectations. What we expect, we are likely to get. Just like American industrialist Henry Ford is famous for saying: "If you think you can do a thing or think you can't do a thing, you're right."

Do you say to yourself, "I would love to . . ." (complete that sentence with anything you really want)? And then do you turn around and say to yourself, "But that probably won't happen because of x, y, or z"? Humans in general always think of reasons why NOT. Why it WON'T work. Why we CAN'T.

But what about asking yourself, "If I really want this (do I really want this?), then how am I am going to make it happen?"

Are you someone who often thinks of the worst-case scenario and you feel that's being wise and safe? Sometimes, ignorance can be bliss and often NOT knowing all the details saves you from expecting the worst.

To come full circle on my birth stories, if I had not heeded the wise words of my doula, and instead of being open and curious, I worried day and night, had low expectations of my body's capacity to give birth, imagined and memorized my interpretation of the pain other women had while giving birth, and told myself how awful the experience was going to be— how do you think my birth experience might have turned out?

This is not to say that if some mothers had a rough birthing experience they were in any particular way responsible. I am not saying that. But neuroscience research has shown that the brain doesn't know the difference between real and imagined (particularly in the aspect of skill acquisition, pain, and the human motor system).

That being said, if you are fearing the worst pain and bracing for it in advance, by imagining the great pain you will be in, your body, whether through a conscious clenching or unconscious usurping, will tighten and your baby will have a harder time getting through the birth canal when the time does come.

This can happen in the weeks leading up to birthing also, as you play it like a movie in your mind. Again, simply fearing the experience is not causation for a long labor, hours of pushing, needing an emergency C-section, or otherwise, by no means, but perhaps a correlation that can inform us as to the importance of calming visualizations or other techniques for birth preparation.

FITMAMA FOUNDATION: Avoid reinforcing the stereotype and sparking the fires of a pregnant woman's fears by telling her how painful/long/ horrible it was for you.

Do you realize the impact you have on others?

Let me put it this way: Why would you ever tell someone a horror story about a scenario they are going to be going through? It makes NO sense. You will only do it if your ego wants to make you feel better by seeing someone else suffer.

Please stop doing that.

Feeling better about yourself by putting other people down makes nobody feel better in the end.

FITMAMA FOUNDATION: They may forget what you said, but they will never forget how you made them feel (Carl W. Buechner).

We often lower our expectations or lower our standards, just so we don't get disappointed. We go into yearly holiday events thinking, "Ugh, another year and this family member's going to be bad again. Uncle Will, he always makes comments that trigger me to eat too much." We lower our expectations, and we come from that place of a fixed mindset.

According to psychology professor Carol Dweck and her research on mindset, she recommends creating the alternative, a growth mindset. So, when you are in a fixed mindset, you keep your expectations low. I urge you to start to come from that mindset to the growth mindset in every aspect of your life, where you realize that everything that you have going on your life has the ability to be different than it is. You are not a victim of chance, and you can come to each encounter in your life with an expectation that it can be different. You will learn new habits, you can be in the best shape of your life after kids, you can love your body, and all that you want is possible for yourself.

Even with things that you think are not going to change, "Ugh, that's never going to change, it's always going to be like that," they do. Things change fast, and they often change a lot faster and maybe in a different way than we thought they would, but if we set our intentions and do the work, things will change the way we want them to change. Mark my words—getting into that growth mindset and maximizing your expectations will absolutely change your life for you.

Maximize your expectations, expect the most massive, incredible things in your life, because why not? "If anyone can do it, I can too." This is always something I say to myself.

FITMAMA FOUNDATION: If anyone can do it, I can too.

You are no better or no worse than anybody else, but it's all about coming into each moment with a blank slate and that growth mindset of saying, "You know what, it can happen! If someone else can be loving their perfectly imperfect body, or if someone can feel calm and eat freely and do things in life that I have always wanted to do, why can't I?" There will be a way, when there's a will. You have to really want it.

If you've ever said to yourself, "I've always wanted to run a marathon. I've always wanted to go back to school. I've always wanted to x, y, and z." It's time to start dreaming, FitMama! Because I know, for you, anything is possible.

What are those desirable things for you? Not for your ego, but for YOU. What lights you up? Start to maximize those expectations by daydreaming about what's possible for you. Anything. Okay? True, deep transformation in your core comes from maximizing your expectations and getting connected deeper to your values and beliefs.

Value Your Values

As I said earlier, "When you stand for nothing, you will fall for anything," right? What do you stand for? What do you value?

I realized soon after I injured myself that I valued a healthy body, but I didn't value what it took to have that. I didn't value rest and recovery the way I do now.

When you feel deeply connected with your values, your sense of self, and your sense of what you want in your life, your decisions reflect that.

From that grounded place, you get to choose how you want to feel, what you want to do to feel that way, and what actions will best get you there. When you approach your new habits from that grounded place, I guarantee you're not going to feel like bingeing on cake or skipping your workouts. You are going to eat healthy and do your workouts. Because you respect yourself and you've actively listened to the inner you, who wants to align with her values. You're letting yourself be heard. You're becoming the you who doesn't want to buy into societal expectations anymore, but instead wants to live a higher-vibe life by creating greater expectations for yourself that reflect your values.

While it doesn't happen overnight, one little situation leads to the next little situation of you embracing your feelings, whether they are loneliness, fatigue, anger, resentment, or whatever. And you say out loud, "This is not how I wanted it to be; I want to change it now."

Are you ready? If you are reading this, I know the answer is yes.

Tell yourself, "From this point on, I'm going to do this instead. This is going to be my new habit." And then follow through. Hold yourself to it, get deeper into your why, and just do it.

Every time you see yourself returning to those old habits, you can remind yourself to rehearse and rewire. It starts that cycle and keeps it moving. Each little piece of insight or awareness that you open up to, you can stop yourself and choose a new action. If you stay connected with your daily breathing practice and stay present, you will notice yourself and then catch it, "Oh, I'm going back to those old ways. Okay, what am I going to do? What am I going to do to switch that around?"

These tools are available to you and when they are wired to be at the top of your mind, because you're journaling about it, meditating, breathing, or moving, they can be your biggest ally.

I remember how aware I was to not let the negative stories people told me sink into my subconscious mind. When people would tell me scary, horror stories about their births or painful stories about labors that lasted for days, I would choose not to let that become part of me. I am an empath, in the true sense of the word, and because I am sensitive to others' energies, I have the tendency to take on others' pain as my own.

I had to close my ears and my mind to something bad happening to me or the baby. I can't listen to people describing graphic things. When I took sports injuries classes, I used to have to leave when there were signs of images and videos of bones popping through skin and blood anywhere. It was like I could feel it in my own body and I felt ill.

Was I living with my head in the clouds, thinking that a hard childbirth would never happen to me? Was it possible that I would have a two-day labor? Sure. But ruminating about it for months wasn't going to help change it. Was it possible my hips weren't wide enough, or things wouldn't progress fast enough, or I might need emergency surgery? Yes, but I excluded it from penetrating my personal protective field, where inside I kept my observations open. I was open if that was to be my story, but also open to experiencing a different one.

The difference here is approaching the world through curiosity. Be curious about your motivations, curious about your fears. Not so much through avoiding fear, but by friending it, so to speak, and asking what it's there to teach you. Because there are great lessons to be learned from fear.

As mentioned previously, Carol Dweck, author of *Mindset: The New Psychology of Success,* has become well known for her work on the concept of a "growth" mindset versus a "fixed" mindset. I am loving this concept and she is opening the minds of many through her brilliant work. I talk about growth versus fixed mindset in the FitMama Foundations™ program.

My husband, Chris, brought it to my attention, as he teaches it to coaches that he trains through his basketball training and coach development website (www.basketballimmersion.com). We teach it to our daughters by praising their *efforts* and not their results: ("I see you put great effort into drawing that rainbow!" versus "Great job!"). This allows them to expand the possibilities they see for themselves by realizing effort is the winning factor, not the job itself.

Learn to approach things with open expectations for how they might be, not low expectations based on your past experiences or what others are talking about. Open your mind, as if anything were possible. This is the first question I ask FitMamas: "If anything were possible, what would your life look like?"

Sometimes the answer I get is, "I don't know."

I call bullshit on that.

Pardon me? What?! "I don't know" is not even an answer.

If you really don't know what you want or why you want something, you most certainly are not going to be getting it or living the life you want.

The first step in maximizing your expectations is idealizing. Let yourself daydream, but within realistic parameters that you can work with. Write it all down in your journal. Be honest with yourself, and don't shut down any lines of thought because "it'll never happen." Get out of your head and onto paper the shitty first draft (SFD as Brené Brown calls it) of what's going on for you and be okay that it's going to be a little messy. Then start penning ideas and dreams that feel good in your body. That feel good in your soul. My friend, coach and colleague Kimberley Banfield, of the Soul Purpose Project, helped me with this immensely. I had no idea what it meant to listen to my soul, trust my intuition and start letting go of things that were holding me back for good. I didn't even realize this was such a missing link in my life.

Once you have it all on paper, take a step back, and look at it through open eyes. There will be at least one thing in there you can start making concrete plans to achieve. Ask yourself if it's just something you want to talk about or think about or whether you are ready to take action. Is it the right time? Have integrity and follow through with creating real plans and action steps, if it is actually something you want.

When you idealize and have integrity, you can commit to work for what you want. And, yes, it takes work. You don't want what you want to come easy. You will value it more if you have to work for it. Resting is hard and pushing is hard. You have to do both at different times. Find a harmony between the two. When you have integrity and you tune in to your intuition, you will have confidence that what you are working for is on its way perfectly on time. And when you idealize and you get more intuitive, you can feel a comforting sense of control from surrendering and seeing the beliefs and behaviors getting you results along the way. You will know you are set up for success on an ongoing basis.

This ideal you, that is relaxed, calm, and content, is confident that you are being the mother, leader, role model, and person you know you can be inside you now, and it's wanting to come out.

I know it can be morbid to consider, but have you ever asked, "What if today were my last day?" How can you start to live your days with less fear and more expectation that good is always coming your way, and this day will never come again? Don't spend it worrying or wishing that things were different. You always have more than enough abundance and love, time, support, money, and happiness available for you.

FITMAMA FOUNDATION: It's the things we DON'T do in life that we regret, more than the things we DO.

I watched my grandfather, whom I admired and revered, die a relatively quick and painful death. From his stomach cancer diagnosis to surgery to passing it was only six months. I recall vividly chatting with him one on one, and on his deathbed literally weeks before he was gone, at the age of 75, he was questioning it all—his whole life. "Should I have lived differently?" he asked me.

He unraveled his whole life before me and then and there I knew, I couldn't help him in this moment, and I never wanted to feel as helpless as he felt right then. He wondered if he ever did anything he truly wanted, or lived by what others wanted for him. I didn't want to live for others' expectations. I was choosing instead to dive inward, and I could tell, even back then, that it was the only way out.

People always ask me, "How do I increase my expectations and believe in myself more? I have always told myself how bad I am at sports and activities and how out of shape I will always be."

It is all too common in our society that we have a low sense of self-worth. That we think others are better than us, or know more than us, or will always look better than us.

Marketers take advantage of this, and though our parents did the best they could, we still were likely raised with a sense of lack in our lives.

Get out of the lack mentality. Lack begets more lack, and if you think others have to fail for you to succeed, or there is not enough awesome to go around, you will stay stuck for life.

When was the last time you daydreamed about more alone time? When was the last time you acted on it and scheduled it? Why haven't you yet? You know you need it. Do you daydream about travel, or things you want to do, but then quash your own dreams? Don't do that to yourself. Start taking time daily to daydream of your ideal reality and then start to see how the images and movies of that ideal that you play in your mind start to become your reality.

Daydreaming allowed me to see in my mind's eye that a fear-free birth without complications was possible for me, but along with staying open and curious, I decided I needed to take further action and *do something*. One thing I became aware of when I journaled about this was that I was living in fear of the pain. I was having paralysis by analysis, and it was a couple of weeks before my first daughter was born that I was still feeling that clenching and thinking, "oh, my, how am I going to get this baby out?"

I believe it was 2009, when my friend, Jackie (the same friend who took me on the Vipassana 10-day silent meditation retreat), first told me about the emotional freedom technique (EFT). Jackie had gone through a breast cancer diagnosis and aggressive treatment protocol and had said that it really helped her let go of fear and negative emotions.

I thought it sounded great. And I met a local woman, named Kelly, who did it. When I was trying to figure out how to get through my fear of birthing, a couple of years later, I decided to give Kelly a call and see if she could help me.

I clearly remember being in her house, on Wednesday of the week my daughter was born on Friday. We sat in her office and performed tapping all over my head and torso in a sequence that was designed to clear the negative emotions and allow me freedom from the fear. I told her what I wanted to experience and we tapped about how much I loved myself, regardless of the outcome. I left and remember feeling more relaxed immediately.

This is a technique I still use and I was so confident that it helped me have a quick and uncomplicated birth, that I did a Skype session with Kelly before my second daughter was born. Again, I was fortunate to have a great labor and delivery, from start to finish my labor was about 75 minutes. Due to road construction, my husband, both midwives, my good friend (and doula), Jessica, all arrived about 3:45 p.m. that day, and she was born at 4:06 p.m. Things moved quickly, and I was grateful I had decided to have a home birth for our second child, after last time's horrific ride to the hospital across town while fully dilated. I did not want to repeat that.

The science behind EFT is fascinating, as Harvard Medical School found that tapping in this way stimulates the body's meridian points and reduces activity in the amygdala, which is the part of the brain that processes emotional reactions, specifically fear. WOW! I had no idea at the time what an incredible tool I had tapped into (pun intended).

Furthermore, the amygdala processes memory and decision making and releases copious amounts of cortisol (the stress hormone) into the bloodstream. Another reason not to tune in to all those negative fear-mongering moms trying to get you to join their pity party. Perhaps if you hear someone telling their horror stories suggest they might benefit from journaling about their experience to get it out for good, and maybe do some tapping to reduce the fear response it keeps evoking inside them when they think about it. Studies have shown tapping to reduce blood cortisol levels by up to 50 percent. Create the opportunity to make better decisions by reducing the stressful reactive way of being that is triggered by fear.

Last, dare to not compare yourself to others. Your birth being fast, drug free, or whether you gained or lost the weight the way you wanted doesn't make you any better or less amazing. Aim high and commit to what you know you are capable of. Looking at others, and thinking they are better than you, is a waste of precious resources. Someone will always be better, someone will always be worse. Someone will always be richer, happier, smaller, bigger, crazier, or seem more blessed than you. Let that go and just be the best you every day, so that you can fall asleep at night and wake up each morning with a calm, compassionate heart filled with reverence for all life and this starts with yourself.

Letting go of others' expectations and adopting more positive, encouraging, uplifting ones for yourself is the key to setting a solid FitMama Foundation for life. Get deeply rooted in your core, knowing you deserve the best that is available to you. You are entitled to it, and you will be living that dream if you let yourself. Don't stand in your own way, or let that little voice in your head let you think your fears are real.

Your beauty and brilliance is real.

Let it shine.

LOVE FITMAMA CHAPTER TAKEAWAY

1. Daydream daily by giving yourself inspiring images and movies in your head detailing what's possible for your ideal life.

2. Do something. Just daydreaming will not have the effects you want without taking action. Action cures fear.

3. Dare to not compare yourself to others. You are not them, they are not you. Focus on being the best you that you can be, and start noticing how much comparing leaves you feeling powerless.

CHAPTER 12

Managing Obligations: "You Can Say No, You Know?"

"No is a complete sentence.
It doesn't require justification or explanation."

—Unknown

This is one of those last, but not least, essential pieces of the puzzle of core transformation. The Love FitMama Way is a way to approach motherhood that both absolves you from responsibility for things that you don't need to be taking on and simultaneously calls you to be a higher version of yourself, by having you take on more responsibility for your life and how it's playing out.

Absolve yourself now, from taking on the responsibility of pleasing everyone around you, of being the best at everything, and of caring what others think. I know in my heart you are an amazing person, even without knowing you yet. I know you don't do anything to purposely hurt someone. You know that too. So, don't worry about being seen as a bad person, or lazy, rude, uncaring, etc. Because you aren't those things. So, just be you!

It's time to set boundaries, and sometimes this is the hardest thing to do. We are raised to be "nice" and "kind" and be available to everyone all the time. We seek validation from others and justify ourselves by how others see us. We don't realize that how people treat us is the way we've taught them to. It's hard to see that, when we feel taken advantage of or burdened.

In addition to people pleasing, guilt has become the new thing for moms, as we do more than ever and always feel pulled in a million directions. We are left asking, "Was that the best choice I could have made? I should have done this instead." The guilt and shame we feel if our actions are not widely accepted as "the best" will paralyze us and have us do things that will ultimately lead us to feeling a deep level of crazy. Bottle feeding or breastfeeding, co-sleeping or baby in another room, daycare or no daycare, and the list goes on.

We are made sometimes to think that we are harming our baby if we don't do what everyone around us is doing. Listen to the little voice deep in your heart and gut, and make decisions that you can live with today. Today is what matters, don't catastrophize and imagine the worst all the time. Think things through, ask for advice and support from trusted sources, and, at the end of the day, trust yourself to make the decision that is best for you.

Guilt, shame, and regret will release those same stress hormones in your body and will leave you feeling worse the more you ruminate, place blame, or shame yourself or others

There was a study that came out a few years ago, which assessed the feelings of guilt about eating chocolate cake. The researchers found that those who felt guilty about eating chocolate cake (rather than those seeing it as a celebration) felt less control about their eating, were less likely to lose weight, and were less likely to maintain their weight over time. Yes, feeling guilt, shame, or regret about food will not serve you to eat healthier over time. There are no motivating properties about guilt and shame. They only serve to degrade us. The Love FitMama Way is a plea to never degrade yourself. Approach yourself always with love and compassion.

As the leader of your family, along with your partner, you get to choose the foods your family eats and how booked you want your schedule to be. You get to choose how many sports or activities you want your children to be a part of. You get to choose how many events or social things you want to do, and you can say no to anything that doesn't truly light you up or make you feel good. That's the freedom you have!

You are an adult who can make her own decisions. It's time to own that and not ever "feel bad" again. You cannot make others feel bad, it's their personal choice to do so. Don't take that responsibility on yourself. Start exercising your right to say no or assert yourself and ask for what you want and need. Don't agree to everything for everyone else's sake. Self-preservation is needed in this case. Make an agreement with yourself to start honoring your wishes and assessing what it is you want your life to represent. You have the choice to NOT choose the helpless victim role. Woe is not you.

If you're like me, you might be realizing that life seems to flow when you let go. During the past 10 years, I have been able to just let go of the control and the need for certain things to be just right, just the way I like them. If you categorize yourself as Type A or if you have tendencies toward perfectionism with rigidity and minute details, I encourage you to start practicing living in the gray, between the black and white. You don't have to do it all yourself, and you don't have to have someone do it all for you. A nice harmony and flow in your life is what you really seek to find. And you will start to find it in setting boundaries. People pleasing can truly break you down in the long run. You cannot be everything to everyone!

FITMAMA FOUNDATION: Saying no saves sanity.

Boundaries are a huge part of what I teach in the FitMama Foundations™ training program, because it is so common to tune out our own needs as we dial into everyone else's. Being a mom heightens this. People can start to take advantage of us, especially our kids or partners, and we can begin to resent them over time. The important thing to realize if you feel this way is that you are to blame. If others are treating you poorly or taking advantage of you, and you've allowed it to continue, it is up to you to change that. You created that dynamic, and only you can change it.

FITMAMA FOUNDATION: You teach others how to treat you.

When we bring into focus the idea that WE are responsible for our lives, regardless of who is to blame, it is up to us to take back control of your boundaries. But first, it's time for a big self-hug! When others treat us badly, or we have too many obligations we've committed to, we often feel frustrated, angry, resentful, and overwhelmed. This isn't a time to put yourself down more by self-loathing, regret, shame, and so on. It's a time for love and gratitude for yourself. Be grateful that you came to this conclusion now and not 10, 20, or 40 years from now. YAY! It's time to take care of YOU, FitMama.

How liberating is it to know that if you can start setting clearer boundaries for yourself, and those around you, things will start to feel better? You will start to notice that others follow suit when you start to respect yourself and your needs more.

Those you love want you to be happy and feel good. Their quality of life depends on it.

You cannot be everything to everyone.

I share a meme that says, "I'm sorry I've been a crappy friend, I've been busy being an awesome mom." Again, this references the "mom guilt." "I'm sorry I've been a crappy friend, I've been busy being an awesome mom." I love it, because again it references the "mom guilt," right? It comes in, whether or not it's about kids, and we get that massive mom guilt thinking, "Oh, my friends are going to be so mad. I said no to this party, and I couldn't go out there, and I had to stay with my kids. I had no sitter . . . blah, blah, blah," and we feel bad about it.

It's time to drop that, please. Drop that now because you know, that you CAN say no. And you know you are the leader of your own life. Furthermore, if that friend, or those friends, or those people, somehow gets mad at you because you're being an awesome mom or because you need a break from too many obligations, these are NOT your people! Are those really the friends you want to be hanging around with?

Saying no takes practice. It doesn't come easy, if you haven't been doing it. It has to be practiced with consistency. It can't be, "Okay, next time they ask me, I'll say no." Then it comes around, and you "feel bad" and then you go "Oh, okay, all right," and then you go through those same old motions.

The key thing with this is setting boundaries and sticking to them. What are the things that you really need to set for yourself, in your world? And they don't need to be like declarative, like, "Hey, everyone! I'm doing this, and I'm not coming to any of your parties this year." It doesn't have to be like that, it just has to be subtle and only for you.

Shifting your energy around you will protect your space. Create an image, and remember that you can have a little dome of calm that houses you. You can imagine yourself in a little bubble, suspended in a hammock, or in a little teardrop just hanging out in this little space. It's all yours. No one can penetrate because that's yours, and you're starting to set those boundaries.

Then as you become more comfortable, push those boundaries a little wider, if you're feeling fenced in. Pull back again when you start to notice you're feeling like you have too many obligations and you can't (don't want to) manage them all. This is a simple thing to start to notice, when you're being pulled in too many directions.

Then you might notice that even in your kids' lives, you're over involving yourself. Do they need you to pick their clothes, help with homework, or dress them? They might be able to do these tasks themselves, or you might be able to ask for help. Remove yourself and the importance your ego feels when you feel needed. Connect on a different level.

Be sure that you don't create the feeling of guilt about taking your own space. It's a choice to feel guilt. Your space is necessary. So, start to assess your obligations. Look at your week at a glance. I have it in my *Passion Planner*, and it's highlighted in different colors that show me at a glance because I have a color for "me time," which is usually Pilates or meditation, journaling, running, or walking.

Then ask yourself, "Okay, how much time do I have for me? Because I need at least this many hours every day for these things for myself to keep up the high-performance lifestyle that I want to live." You CAN design this. I know, because I do it. And everybody's life sounds so different, but looking at your own for a moment, ask yourself, "What do I want it to look like?"

You need to assess your values and goals. And once you can assess them, you can assign yourself to either say no to more things or you can start to say yes to things that you want to do. Arrange to have someone else do the things that you don't want to do.

Delegate some of your jobs. "Yeah, okay, I could stay home and do laundry, but hubby can fold the laundry while he's watching the game on Friday night." Asking for help and demanding support from kids or partners is key to the household running. It's the 21st century, so this should not all be your responsibility.

FitMama, assign things to others. Enlist help and support. Others can take on some responsibility; it doesn't have to fall only on you. You don't need to DO things every minute of every day. Especially not for people who can do things for themselves. Yes, support them, love them, and nurture them. But just not at your own expense.

FITMAMA FOUNDATION: Feeling guilty is a choice you can choose not to make.

A key factor is asking for help. Assigning people things when you are unavailable (because you scheduled personal time in your planner is a valid reason), and ask others to support you in ways that allow you to practice accepting help. It's one of the toughest things to do. I still struggle with this. I always think I can just do it myself, not bother someone else, and that will be easier. It is, sometimes in the short term, but ultimately it works against you. Remember that you teach people how to treat you. And most people will just do the bare minimum when you are maxing out.

When you ask for help, though, then you're opening yourself up to receive. And you give others permission to ask for help and receive help too.

So often we want to check a personal supermom status box, where we say through words or actions, "I don't need help. I can do it. Don't worry, I got it. You know, my way is best." We just want to do it all. We want to control it all, and we never ask for help. Then, we lament, "Nobody's helping me! Why is everyone sitting around while I am running around like a crazy person?" And the response is, "Well, you haven't ever asked for help, and you made it seem like you wanted to do it all yourself." When we do this, we don't even open that door to receive.

By assigning responsibilities to others that lightens the load for you, you can start to see where you can help others without spreading yourself too thin. What are your needs? What are your responsibilities? While you assign others the tasks that don't fit in these categories, be scrupulous and choose wisely.

Gone are the days, we offer rashly, "I will make the cake, I will throw the party, or I will be there with bells on!" unless we truly and deeply desire that. Sometimes we react so quickly in our people-pleasing natures, so start to lay down new neural pathways that include taking a few deep breaths before speaking (I am working on this one).

Begin by looking at how your needs, wants, and responsibilities all interact.

Obligations

When you look at your needs and responsibilities specifically, it's imperative you assign priority to each, and find places for these in your schedule. Stay organized by spending even 20 minutes on the weekend looking into the week ahead and preparing for it. Get out your agenda or calendar and pencil in time for your grocery shopping, doctor appointments, cooking, prepping, taking on family matters, etc.

Ask for help where the responsibilities start to cut into your wants and some things are not a priority for YOU to do, but you can ask someone else to help with. Does hubby plays hockey weekly or go to a biking club? Does he go on hunting or golf trips? What are *you* doing that fills you up?

So often, we make time for others' need or wants and take responsibility off them and place it on ourselves. It can become our norm. Who can you get more help from? Asking for help is vital when it comes to managing your obligations. You don't need to do it all alone. That is not a badge of honor; that is a badge of bad judgment.

Really assess the crossover between needs and wants. Just like with our finances, we can't always get what we want exactly when we want it, so too this goes for doing what we want, whenever we want it (as if having a baby didn't teach you that). What is a priority right now? Take the time to assess this question honestly and repeatedly. Are things playing out the way you want, and what role do you play in that? Are you sabotaging yourself, and is there something you can start, stop, or change in some way?

Life is constantly changing. As you can recall when you thought you were getting into a routine with your baby, and then she/he regressed in sleep, or changed feeding patterns, or wanted this food and not that. We need to remain flexible, as only then in the center of the needs, wants, and responsibilities is that happy place where you are managing your obligations. Obligations managed = OM. OM can be a word or chant for you that represents a place of peace and calm.

This is truly what's at the center of the Love FitMama Way. It's a flourishing place where all your life feels in harmony with the world. You're in flow, you're enjoying the moments of your life, and you have found that patience, permission, and presence we talked about in Part 1: Embrace: Heed Your Needs.

We have the power to make the changes we want, and it starts from love and acceptance within. To manage your obligations, start with practicing asserting yourself. At first, it will feel a little uncomfortable if you are used to taking on others' feelings. But soon, you will be managing all you have on your plate with a deep sense of peace and awareness.

Start noticing that changes are going to have to be made if things feel out of control for you. Assess your needs and wants and accept that the changes will create new opportunities for you to set boundaries that will strengthen your assertiveness muscles. By assessing these items that you are trying to control your environment (in a noncontrolling, surrendered type of way), decide where you want to put your boundaries.

Start by getting a clear understanding of where you are bleeding time. I get the idea of being a busy new mom tending to everyone, but if you're buried, whom can you ask for help? Where can you become more efficient? Where can you prioritize better? Fit in some of your wants, not just catering to needs. Even when you think you have no time, I can assure you, you do.

Asking for help is massively important to you feeling like you can handle your life and starting to make space for yourself. Know you are worthy of others helping you, not just the other way around. Practice asserting yourself using the word "no" more often. We feel pressured to do things day and night, and saying no, or no, thank you, starts to tell others that you are being more selective with your time, what you do, what you put into your body, or where you go. It sets you up to be respected, not walked all over.

Standing up for yourself is a big step, and we don't get taught the details of what it takes. It's not about being condescending or better than others, it's simply saying no to things or events that don't serve you. It's asking for support and help because you need it. We all do.

FITMAMA FOUNDATION: There is no cheating, just choosing.

When it comes to setting boundaries, the language we use to talk to ourselves plays an important role. Do everything in your power to stop using words like cheat, guilt, bad, good, should, have to, or need to. Realize that the words you use toward yourself have deep meaning and imprint on you at the cellular level and subconscious mind. When you tell yourself, you've been "good" today because you ate your veggies, you're subconsciously telling yourself how "bad" you are when you decide otherwise.

Don't degrade yourself by talking negatively toward yourself. EVER. Just don't do it. Along with that, let go of allowing others to make you feel a certain way. Remember First Lady Eleanor Roosevelt's quote, "No one can make you feel inferior without your consent," and stop feeling guilty if you did or didn't do something. Let that energy motivate you to get it done next time—guilt free. Foods are labeled now, "guilt free," like they have the permission to dictate how you feel about a food. Do not let this be dictated for you! Feel no guilt when it comes to food at all.

One of the last concepts I will leave you with for now, as the Love FitMama Way concludes, is this: *tune in.*

Tune in to the voice that your body is using to talk to you. It's communicating all day, every day. Slow down, close your eyes and your lips, and just listen.

Question that negative, berating tone you might have used in the past and trust that you won't get where you want to go by listening to it any longer.

You cannot create love from hate.

Open up to that unconditionally, loving inner you who is like a small child. As you notice yourself falling into old patterns, go over to her, have a conversation, give her a hug, and say, "It's okay, you've been doing/thinking that way for 20, 30, or 50 years, so it's natural you would go back to that, but we have a new way now, the Love FitMama Way.

Just speak to yourself to embrace every little part of you, nurture this beautiful and perfect you, and enjoy this journey you are on, because as you know, once you are a mom, you are always a mom. Relish at the opportunity to truly transform the whole core of your being to reflect the values and beliefs YOU have NOW, not the ones you adopted mindlessly while growing up, being busy, or obliging to "authorities."

"Life is what happens to you while you are busy making other plans" (Allen Saunders).

If you remember nothing else from this book, remember to—

Breathe: Daily take time to connect mindfully to your current body and your current reality. Let go of expectations and embrace you today.

Breathe: Learn and routinely practice Pearl Pull-Ups™ and deep-core breathing, as your opportunity to create greater strength in the core of your body to grow the roots of your life.

Breathe: Open your mind and your eyes to all the beauty and magic in your life. Be grateful for every ounce of your body, inside and out. And commit to never speak negatively toward yourself again.

Have unconditional love and reverence for your body and life and cherish each moment you are alive.

Yes, you can.

Just breathe.

That is The Love FitMama Way.

LOVE FITMAMA CHAPTER TAKEAWAY

1. Assign priority to all the responsibilities and needs in your life. Are they all really that important? What can you let go of?

2. Assess what tasks or activities you need to do and which tasks or activities other people can do. You don't have to do them all.

3. Ask for help. You cannot do it all alone, nor does it make you better for trying to prove you can. You're supporting so many others, you will start to resent them if you don't receive help in return.

Suggested Reading List: The Love FitMama Way

A New Earth: Awakening to Your Life's Purpose
    Eckhart Tolle

A Whole New Mind: Why Right-Brainers Will Rule the Future
    Daniel H. Pink SEP

Anatomy of the Spirit: The Seven Stages of Power and Healing
    Caroline Myss SEP

Authentic Happiness: Using the New Positive Psychology to Realize Your Potential for Lasting Fulfillment
    Martin E. P. Seligman SEP

Be Here Now
    Ram Dass SEP

Better Than Before: What I Learned about Making and Breaking Habits—to Sleep More, Quit Sugar, Procrastinate Less, and Generally Build a Happier Life
    Gretchen Rubin

Change Your Thoughts—Change Your Life: Living the Wisdom of the Tao
Wayne W. Dyer

Crazy Sexy Cancer Survivor: More Rebellion and Fire for Your Healing Journey
Kris Carr and Marianne Williamson

Excuses Begone! How to Change Lifelong, Self-Defeating Thinking Habits
Wayne W. Dyer

Flourish: A Visionary New Understanding of Happiness and Well-being
Martin E. P. Seligman ⌜SEP⌟

Flow: The Psychology of Optimal Experience
Mihaly Csikszentmihalyi ⌜SEP⌟

Healthy at 100: The Scientifically Proven Secrets of the World's Healthiest and Longest-Lived Peoples
John Robbins

How to Eat, Move and Be Healthy!
Paul Chek ⌜SEP⌟

Man's Search for Meaning, Viktor E. Frankl ⌜SEP⌟

My Stroke of Insight: A Brain Scientist's Personal Journey
Jill Bolte Taylor ⌜SEP⌟

Prepare to Push: What Your Pelvic Floor and Abdomen Want You to Know about Pregnancy and Birth
Kim Vopni

Rising Strong: How the Ability to Reset Transforms the Way We
   Live, Love, Parent, and Lead
   Brené Brown

The Alchemist
   Paulo Coelho [L][SEP]

The Four Agreements: A Practical Guide to Personal Freedom
   Don Miguel Ruiz and Janet Mills

The Omnivore's Dilemma: A Natural History of Four Meals
   Michael Pollan [SEP]

The Power of Intention: Learning to Co-create Your World Your Way
   Wayne W. Dyer

The Power of Now: A Guide to Spiritual Enlightenment
   Eckhart Tolle

The Subtle Art of Not Giving a F*ck: A Counterintuitive
   Approach to Living a Good Life
   Mark Manson

The Surrender Experiment: My Journey into Life's Perfection
   Michael A. Singer

The Tipping Point: How Little Things Can Make a Big Difference
   Malcolm Gladwell [L][SEP]

The UltraMind Solution: Fix Your Broken Brain by Healing
   Your Body First
   Mark Hyman

The Untethered Soul: The Journey beyond Yourself
   Michael A. Singer [L][SEP]

Wherever You Go, There You Are: Mindfulness Meditation in Everyday Life
Jon Kabat-Zinn [SEP]

Wisdom of the Ages: A Modern Master Brings Eternal Truths into Everyday Life
Wayne W. Dyer [SEP]

Within: A Spiritual Awakening to Love and Weight Loss
Habib Sadeghi [SEP]

Women, Food, and God: An Unexpected Path to Almost Everything
Geneen Roth

You Are the Placebo: Making Your Mind Matter
Joe Dispenza

You Can Heal Your Life
Louise L. Hay

Your Pelvic Floor—The Inside Story: Education and Wisdom from Pelvic Health Professionals across the Globe
Kim Vopni

Healing Back Pain: The Mind-Body Connection
John E. Sarno

Loving What Is: Four Questions That Can Change Your Life
Byron Katie

Breaking the Habit of Being Yourself: How to Lose Your Mind and Create a New One
Joe Dispenza

Big Magic: Creative Living beyond Fear
  Elizabeth Gilbert

Start with Why: How Great Leaders Inspire Everyone to Take Action
  Simon Sinek

Stumbling on Happiness
  Daniel Gilbert

Learned Optimism: How to Change Your Mind and Your Life
  Martin E. P. Seligman

Mindset: The New Psychology of Success
  Carol S. Dweck

*The 5 Second Rule: Transform Your Life, Work and Confidence
  with Everyday Courage*
  Mel Robbins

About the Author

Jen Oliver was born and raised in Toronto, then moved to Ottawa for part of her high school years. Formerly known as Jen Bittner, she studied and played Varsity Basketball at Queen's University in Kingston, Ontario, Canada. Jen graduated with a degree in Physical and Health Education and Psychology and then a couple of years later, went on to get a Master's Degree in Exercise and Health Psychology at McMaster University in Hamilton, Ontario. Jen's big heart, her positive spirit and love for helping others has allowed her to help thousands of private clients over the last 15 years. Over that time and most especially that last 5 years, Jen has created many programs and resources specifically for FitMamas. Jen currently works solely online with clients and when she isn't traveling, she resides in Windsor, Ontario with her husband Chris and two daughters, Kennedy and Presley. Please find more on Jen and her work at lovefitmama.com

Made in the USA
Columbia, SC
09 April 2018